100 YEARS OF AMERICA'S

FIRE FIGHTING
APPARATUS

100 YEARS OF AMERICA'S
FIRE FIGHTING APPARATUS

BY PHIL DA COSTA

BONANZA BOOKS · NEW YORK

This edition published by Bonanza Books,
a division of Crown Publishers, Inc.,
by arrangement with Floyd Clymer Publications.

C   D   E   F   G   H

Manufactured in the United States of America

SOURCES OF INFORMATION

I want to express my sincerest gratitude and appreciation to all the wonderful people, manufacturers, Fire Service personnel and my close friends who have contributed material and for their kind permission to use it. Their responsive participation and interest have broadened the prospect of making this book a success. To them and to all the fire fighters of the world, I graciously dedicate this book. It is my profound wish that this book will remain a pictorial memory of our fabulous fire engines from the romantic days of horses to the colorful moments of motor propelled apparatus. May they never be forgotten.

PHIL DA COSTA - Author

Photos-Catalogs	Mr. A. L. Denton — American La France Corp. — Elmira, N.Y.
Photos-Catalogs	Mr. P. V. Hamilton — Mack Truck — Los Angeles Division
Photos	Mr. C. A. Carey — Maxim Motor Co. — Milborough, Mass.
Photos	Mr. R. A. Fryer — White Motor Co. — Cleveland, Ohio
Photos-Catalogs-Ads	Mr. Andrew Ayres — Seagrave Corp. — Columbus, Ohio
Scale Drawings	Mr. Jack Ruggles — Seagrave Corp. — Los Angeles Div.
Photos Fire Dept. Manual	Chief Wm. Murray — San Francisco Fire Dept.
Scale Drawings of S.F.F.D. — Al Flaherty — Supt. of Shops	
Photos-Scale Drawings	Capt. Tom Showers — Los Angeles Fire Dept.-County
Photos-Historical Data San Francisco, California	Irving "Doc" Levin — Phoenix Society
Photos-Historical Data Museum Engine Co. 23	Capt. Louis Hage — San Francisco Fire Dept.
Photos-Historical Info. Los Angeles Fire Dept.	All members of Eng. Co. 93 Tarzana Station,
Ahren-Fox Photos-Ads	Dale Magee — Member Box 15 Club — Los Angeles, Cal.
Photos of Apparatus — Bob Sams — Birmingham, Alabama	

FOREWORD

This book is the result of a life-long interest in fire apparatus, and the desire to share this interest with others of similar inclination. It was also conceived in a spirit of dedication to those courageous firefighters who are on call day and night, protecting citizens and their property from the disaster that uncontrolled fire can bring.

How many of us have thrilled to the wondrous sounds of bells, sirens and horns as the fire laddies raced to the searing infernos? All of us have watched with awe as the great machines arrived on the scene and their crews, with amazing efficiency, set about their tasks. We have seen all manner of equipment, sometimes spanning several generations, at work on the same fire, and we have wondered why it is that some of these museum pieces are still at work, while other vehicles of the same vintage are in the covetous hands of collectors. The fact of the matter is that fire equipment dies hard, and it is also expensive and not very often replaced except when it is absolutely necessary.

Many spectators behind the fire lines watch the action with breath-taking interest while the determined firemen go about their duties. Yet precious few take notice of the variety of equipment on the scene, and fewer still are aware that some of these machines are worthy of museum display. It is for this reason that this book devotes so much space to types, vintage, manufacturer, and the cities in which certain pieces of apparatus were used.

From the days of hand-drawn pump and ladder trucks until the present time, a great number of manufacturers have specialized in fire fighting equipment. Among these are Seagrave (1881), Maxim (1881), and the American Fire Engine Company, now known as American La France (1880). Following in the footsteps of these great pioneers were many other makers, all of whom have made major contributions to the science of firefighting.

Perhaps the greatest transition came in the 1900's, when the gasoline engine started to make inroads into the American way of life. It was then that horse-drawn equipment began to be replaced. Although at first it was only the horse that was replaced, because much of the equipment was still used, but in place of the horse was a rumbling gasoline powered tractor. Grave doubts surrounded these changes. Could these new machines do the job better than the horse, were they as dependable as a horse, or could they get to the fire faster? How about fuel consumption and maintenance costs? This suspicion of the gas engine even led some of the manufacturers to consider electricity as a power source, and Seagrave produced several aerial ladder trucks so powered, in 1910.

Today, when most of the earlier manufacturers have disappeared into history, this book will serve to recall some of their names. There was Ahrens and Fox, Peter Pirsch, Kissel, Hale, Four Wheel Drive, and a score of others. Some names still remain, like Mack and White, but now the fire engines are just a small part of their total commercial truck output.

It is unfortunate that this book cannot be done in color, because much of the beauty of these machines depended upon their fantastic paint jobs. Red, with gold leaf trim and striping was the usual combination, but there were some magnificent white ones, and maroon was also a favorite color. These fire engines were all put together by precision craftsmen, and the trim was applied by skilled artisans, the like of which are hard to find today. It was usually a matter of civic pride in the early days, to have the most beautiful engine that the city budget could afford. Some cities spent thousands of dollars on their equipment, and this no doubt was one of the major reasons that so much time was taken in their upkeep.

Slowly but surely, many of these old beauties are leaving the scene, and only in museums can one hope to see them in their olden splendor. True, some of them have fallen into the hands of fire engine buffs, but one of the outstanding collections is the famous San Francisco Fire Department Museum, where under the direction of Captain Louis Hage, a large group of relics has been assembled.

Much of the material for this book was taken from the archives of the San Francisco Museum, and since model builders will doubtless use this book as a source of information, I have taken special care to give color schemes where possible, and to include several scale drawings. One of these drawings, the 1910-1915 hook and ladder, were taken from the San Francisco Fire Department's original shop prints. You will note that the original rig was pulled by three white horses, and that the change from horse to engine power only altered the general appearance of the vehicle. The major difference was the replacement of the original hard rubber tires with pneumatics. This rig is still in active service.

You will also find in this book information concerning some of the early water towers from the San Francisco area. Most of these were the result of development by one of the engineers in the fire department, Mr. Gorter. He was also responsible for the development of a ball socket nozzle, which bears his name. As early as 1898 Mr. Gorter had built a 65 foot horse-drawn extension water tower, and by 1902 the height had grown to 75 feet. These were converted to engine-drawn in the early twenties, and are still in service today, one drawn by a 1920 Klieber tractor, and the other by a 1939 Ahren and Fox. The solid tires remained until after World War II, when they were changed to pneumatics. The original dark maroon paint still remains.

Unfortunately many of the manufacturers of old apparatus have destroyed their original prints, but through diligent research I have managed to come up with fairly accurate drawings and dimensions. The catalogs which I have used are extremely rare and out of print, and although this book is by no means complete, it is intended to give a general picture of the period, and to act as a starting point or a guide to those interested in this very fascinating subject.

Phil DaCosta

100 YEARS OF AMERICA'S
FIRE FIGHTING
APPARATUS

ANNOUNCEMENT

In presenting this unique book we feel certain it will appeal to Fire Engine buffs, collectors, enthusiasts and historians. The author, Philip J. DaCosta, is well qualified and a dedicated authority, having been connected with fire departments for many years.

Since I have lived during the period of the transition from hand-drawn, to horse-drawn, to motorized fire equipment, the work of Mr. DaCosta intrigued me. I have always been intensely interested in everything that rolls on wheels or flies through the air. My interest in all kinds of vehicles and forms of transportation has resulted in over 300 different books, which I have written and/or published in the last two decades.

My interest in fire fighting apparatus started when, as a youngster of seven, my father, Dr. J. B. Clymer (a small town physician and surgeon) bought the first automobile to be sold north of Denver in Colorado. The little town of Berthoud nestles up against the majestic Colorado Rocky Mountain range just east of what is now the Rocky Mountain National Park. I learned to drive this curved-dash, 5-horsepower, single-cylinder Oldsmobile when I was seven. By the time I was eleven I was a dealer for Reo, Maxwell and Cadillac cars, and I sold 26 cars in two years.

Soon after the turn of the century fire fighting equipment was purchased by the Berthoud Town Council. It consisted of a horse cart, with perhaps 50 yards of hose wound on a reel, and a few nozzles. This cart, with two wooden-spoked high wheels, carried the paraphernalia; and propulsion was by the athletic men of the town. The ambition of most young men of Berthoud was to become a member of the Berthoud Volunteer Fire Department. There was no salary, no fixed hours, and members totalled about 25. When the alarm sounded the first five to reach the small wooden firehouse were the ones to get into harness to pull the cart, as fast as flying legs could turn the wheels.

The local telephone operator was the clearing house and, as the fire bell continued to ring, other volunteer members hurried to the scene of the fire, when they learned the location from the operator. Sometimes it was weeks or months between fires; however, the members of the team had to keep in practice, so once a week the townspeople lined the streets to watch the boys practice. This consisted of getting into harness and making a run of 200 to 500 yards, hooking up the hose and getting water through the nozzle as fast as possible — and timed by three judges with stop watches. Occasionally kerosene would be poured on a pile of wooden boxes to simulate an actual fire.

Every town in Colorado had Volunteer Departments and at certain times, usually on July 4th or at the Fall County Fairs, teams from several cities would compete against each other to see which team could cover the selected course and get water to the nozzle the fastest. Supporters from each town would come to these events to cheer their favorites on. Sometimes teams from several towns would complete in a series of elimination contests. The finalists would go to the County Fair, or the State Fair in Pueblo, or sometimes to the State Capital of Denver.

For six years Dad was Mayor of Berthoud and I'll never forget a contest when he was lead man on the hose-cart team. He stumbled and fell, taking the other four men down with him, and the cart piled into the fallen men. Results were a few skinned elbows and/or knees and injured pride, for the Berthoud team had won two Northern Colorado Championships.

During his term as Mayor, like all politicians anxious to make good, Dad had an idea to improve the fire department service. By that time there were about ten cars in town. Dad's idea, which he sold to the Council, was to have a trailer hitch attached to the tongue of the hose-cart and each car equipped with what would now be known as a trailer hitch. Thus, when the fire alarm sounded, any one of ten cars could rush to the fire house, hook onto the cart and arrive at the fire much quicker than the cart could when it was necessary for five department team members to show up to get it moving.

Thus the first motorized fire equipment came to our town about 1907. Owners and cars were Ed McCormick's Maxwell, Ed Wray's Reo, George Nall's Ford, Jim Jefferies' Overland, J. Y. Munson's Reo, Lew Hertha's Stanley Steamer, Frank McAllister's Velie, L. D. Orton's Lambert, F. I. Davis' Buick, and Dad's Maxwell.

Actually, Berthoud had motorized Fire Department services before Denver. Dad was the local railroad physician for Colorado and Southern Railroad, thus the family rode on passes. During vacation I usually went to Denver (54 miles) on the early train and returned on the late train every Saturday. I walked along Broadway, which was then (and still is) Denver's Auto Row. But always I would get over near the State Capitol, where there was a fire house near Colfax and Broadway. A team of beautiful black horses stood in stalls alongside the fire wagon. When the alarm sounded the horses, by training and instinct, would stand under the hanging harness which was ready to be dropped down and be connected by firemen. What a sight it was! Even the practice sessions were thrilling and spectacular.

And then came another important transition — the motorized fire trucks to replace the faithful horses. It was about six years or more, however, before trucks replaced the horses — and for some time many stations in cities used both motorized and horse-drawn vehicles. Many firemen of that period were not too sure they could depend on the motorized equipment.

Then came the changeover, with such makes as Seagraves, American LaFrance, Stutz and other makes coming into the picture. I shall never forget when, about 1908 or 1909, Fire Chief Healy of Denver blossomed out with a new fire red Premier Roadster with a large warning bell on the cowl. It was an impressive sight to see the Chief roar over Denver streets ahead of the trucks or horse-drawn units at what then was high speed and with the bell loudly clanging.

In later years the Model T and A Fords came in. Many firms built equipment to fit the Ford chassis. Low prices made it possible for even small towns and residents of rural districts to buy fire fighting equipment to go on a Ford chassis.

And now all large cities have fantastic equipment, and even small cities and towns have excellent units. Even helicopters are used in some regions for fighting grass fires. The changes in fire fighting equipment and techniques that have occurred since the turn of the century have been fantastic and almost unbelievable.

Floyd Clymer

SECTION

I

1898 Bangor Box horse drawn hook and ladder, Portland, Maine. Taken about 1920 during a parade.

1873 Selsby Steam Fire Engine, St. Joseph, Michigan.

100 YEARS 1873 - 1963

1900 Peter Pirsch Hose Wagon for City of Chicago.

1898-1900 American LaFrance Chemical and Hose Wagon, horse-drawn, for City of Chicago.

1879-1881 Earl American LaFrance Hand Drawn Hose Cart.

Forward end of 1909-1910 Seagrave horse-drawn aerial ladder with spring hoist mechanism and hand crank for raising and lowering ladder. Note single driver seat, with gong bell under footrest. Wheels were wooden spoked, tenon and grooved Archibald type with brass hubs.

1898-1905 American LaFrance (Hale) Water Tower #12 in action at Lawrence, Mass. August 16, 1954.

1906 First aerial built by Peter Pirsch for Winnepeg, Canada.

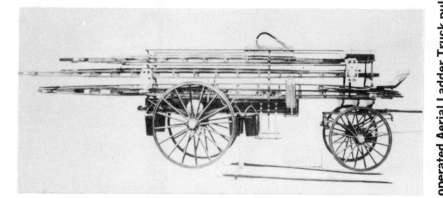

1890 Pirsch Hook and Ladder, horse-drawn, for small town.

1890 Pirsch Hose and Chemical wagon, horse-drawn.

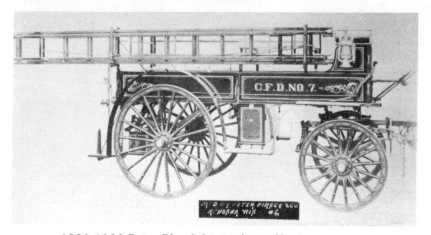

1889-1900 Peter Pirsch horse-drawn Hose wagon.

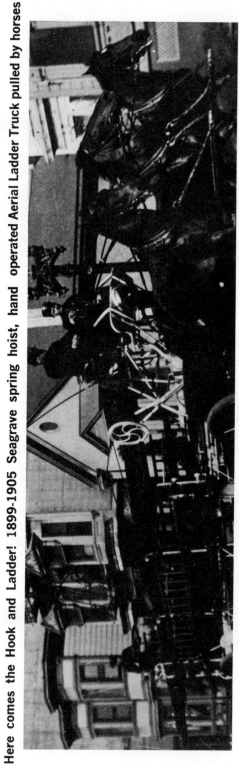

Here comes the Hook and Ladder! 1899-1905 Seagrave spring hoist, hand operated Aerial Ladder Truck pulled by horses

1890-1900 Pirsch horse-drawn Chemical-Hose Reel wagon.

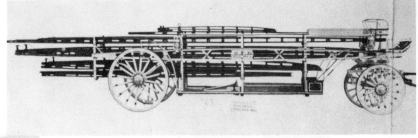

1900 Pirsch horse-drawn Hook and Ladder wagon.

1890-1900 Rear view of Pirsch horse-drawn
Chemical-Hose Reel wagon.

1899-1900 American LaFrance Metropolitan Steam Fire Engine.

1905 Horse-drawn American LaFrance 65 foot Aerial Ladder Truck. Spring hoist, hand crank operated. Color: Ivory, Gold trim.

1898-1900 Racine Chemical Hose Reel, hand-drawn.

1898-1900 Racine Chemical Hose Cart.

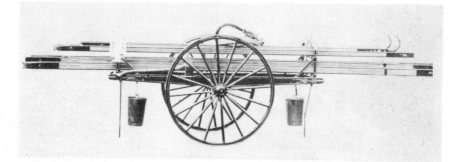

Pirsch hand-drawn two wheel Ladder Cart.

1890 Pirsch Hook and Ladder, hand-drawn.
Made for small village operation.

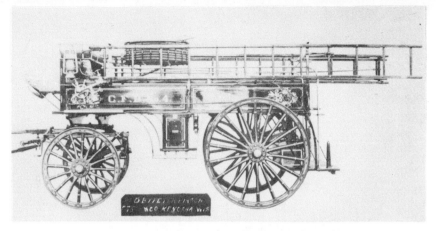

1890 Horse-drawn Pirsch Chemical and Hose Wagon.

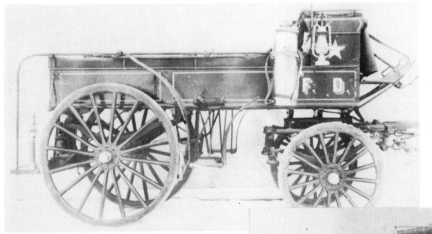

1900 Robinson Hose and Chemical Wagon, horse-drawn.
Built by Robinson Fire Apparatus Manufacturing Co.

1898 Pirsch horse-drawn Hose wagon.

1898-1900 Pirsch horse-drawn
Chemical Hose Reel wagon.

SECTION

II

The famous 1906 Knox 40 h.p. Chemical Car. It carried two 35 gallon Hollaway tanks and 200 feet of 1¼" hose. Top speed was 40 mph.

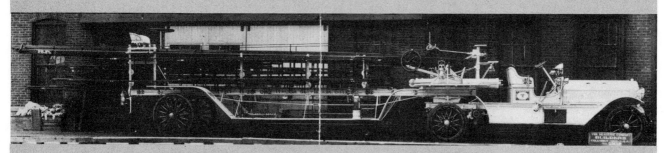

1911-1912 Seagrave 75' Aerial Ladder Truck. Six cylinder, 116 h.p. chain drive. Automatic spring hoist, hand operated, with safety brake. Truck was originally horse-drawn. Ladders carried: 45' extension, and 9' extension, 28' wall, 24' wall, 21' wall, 18' wall, 16' roof, and 12' roof.

One man fire department with Maxim equipment.

**1911 Waterous Pumper and Hose Car as used by the New York City
Fire Department.**

1913 Robinson Aston Pumping Engine and Hose Car, at work.

1913-1915 Ahrens and Fox Pumper and Hose Cart.

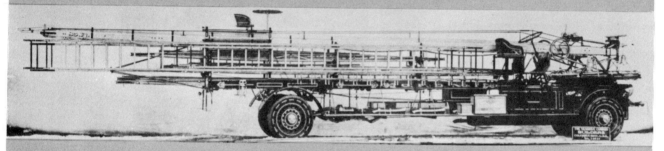

1910 Side saddle steer Seagrave 85' Aerial Ladder Truck. Built for Oakland,
California Fire Department.

1913-1915 Ahrens and Fox Pumper and Hose Cart. Note gong instead of bell,
an odd arrangement for motorized apparatus.

1919 Ahrens and Fox Pumper and Hose Cart. Triple combination, four cylinder.

1913-1914 General Manufacturing Company, St. Louis, Mo. Triple Combination
of Hose, Pumper and Chemical.

15

1915-1917 American LaFrance High Pressure Hose and Pumping Engine. Following behind an early vintage American LaFrance Aerial Ladder, front drive.

1917 Veale Combination Ladder and Chemical Truck. Note similarity to Seagrave and American LaFrance.

1915 Moreland Hose Cart. Behind, the steamer is warming up, pulled by a front drive Christie.

AMERICAN-LAFRANCE

Shatters All Known Pumping Records ▪

Thirteen Days' Continuous Pumping in Zero Weather Adds a New Chapter to the Accomplishments of

American-LaFrance Motor Fire Apparatus

ON November 23rd, 1922, a serious mine fire was discovered at Jonesville, Alaska. To fight the fire a Type 12 American-La France Pumper was summoned from the Anchorage, Alaska, fire department.

It was thirteen days before the fire was extinguished. *During that time the American-LaFrance pumper worked continuously* with the exception of brief stops at irregular intervals for the purpose of changing the oil, and replacing hose that had blown couplings.

To make this performance all the more remarkable, the thermometer at the time of the fire was hovering around the zero mark.

Two hundred pounds pump pressure was maintained, which is equivalent to driving the car 9400 miles at top speed practically without interruption.

Engineering principles evolved from 80 years' experience in building fire apparatus, selection of the best materials, the thorough testing of every car we produce, and superior manufacturing methods, combine to make unusual performances typical of American-La France Motor-Driven Fire Apparatus.

1912 American LaFrance Combination Pump and Hose Wagon. Six cylinder with rotary gear pump. Used by San Francisco Fire Department. Color: Dark maroon.

1911 Mack Piston Pumper
First Gasoline propelled Mack truck

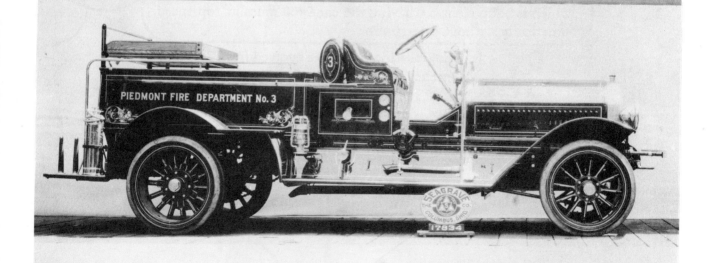

1912-1914 Seagrave 6 cylinder, watercooled, 300 GPM Pumper and Hose Combination. Color Dark maroon.

1912 American LaFrance Chemical and
Hose Reel Car. Built for San Francisco
Fire Department. Color: Maroon and Gold

1912-1914 Close-up detail of Seagrave 4 cylinder, front drive tractor for
steamer. Color: Dark maroon with gold leaf trim.

1913 Seagrave-Gorham Turbine Pumping car. This unique piece of apparatus was the last of the oddities used by the Los Angeles Fire Department. Pump operations were from the rear instead of the sides. This car was originally equipped with solid tires, but was converted to pneumatics in 1944. It was broken up for scrap the following year.

1912-1914 Seagrave Chemical and Hose Car, with extra long overhead ladders. Six cylinder, 110 h.p. watercooled engine. Built for City of Anaheim, California. Color: Dark maroon, gold trim.

1912-1914 American LaFrance 4 cylinder, 75 h.p. Combination Chemical and Hose Wagon as used by City of San Francisco. This car carried 1200 feet of 2½ inch hose, 40 gallon chemical tank with a reel of chemical hose, one 20' extension ladder and one 12' roof ladder with folding hooks. Color: Dark maroon.

1912 American LaFrance Chemical Car of San Francisco Fire Department.

1912-1914 Seagrave 6 cylinder, 110 h.p. Combination Pumper and Hose Car. Color: Dark Maroon.

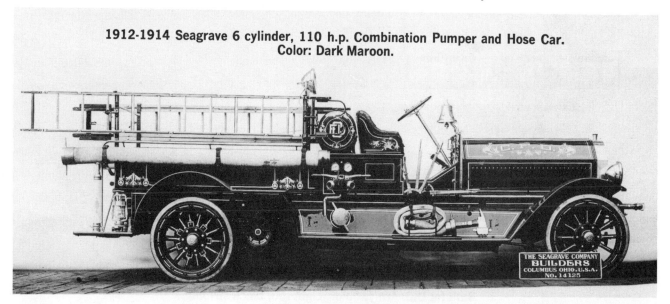

1912-1914 Seagrave Combination Pumper-Chemical and Hose Car. Installation of seats in hose beds is a novel arrangement.

1912-1914 Seagrave Combination Pump and Hose Car. Ladders stowed overhead. Color: White, gold trim.

1912-1914 Seagrave 6 cylinder, 110 h.p. Combination Pumper and Hose Car. Built for U.S. Army. Color: Light red, black striping.

1913-1914 American LaFrance four cylinder Pumping Engine and Hose Car-Chemical Triple Combination.

1913-1914 Seagrave six cylinder, 110 hp, watercooled. 300 gallons per minute (GPM) Pumper and Hose Combination with overhead ladders. Ladders: 20' trussed extension, and 12' roof ladder with folding hooks. Color: Light fire dept. red.

Maxim Combination with Sewel solid tires.

Detail of early pump panel on Maxim Pumper, showing pressure and compound gauges, tachometer and light.

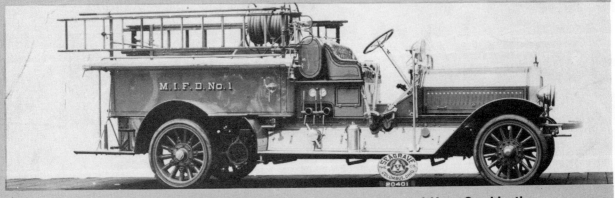

1914 Seagrave 6 cylinder, 116 h.p. chain drive Pumper and Hose Combination with 900 GPM centrifugal pump. Color: Light red with black striping.

Chief of Westerly, Rhode Island with a new Maxim Model F (1914), and an old horse-drawn steamer in tow. Color: Dark maroon.

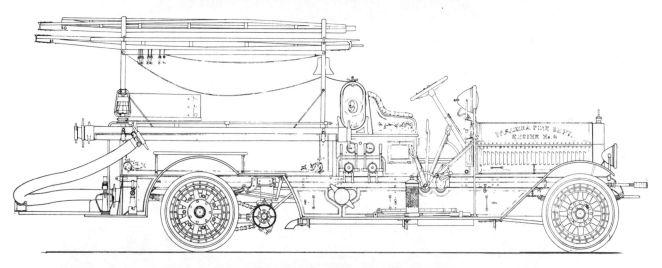

1914 Seagrave Pumper side view drawing.

1914-1915 A six cylinder, 105 h.p. American LaFrance Steam Pumper with front drive tractor as used by San Francisco Fire Department. Color: Dark maroon, gold trim.

1914 Model F Combination Maxim. Four cylinder, chain drive, left hand steering and pneumatic tires. Color: Maroon with gold trim.

**1914 Seagrave 6 cylinder, 110 h.p. Combination Engine and Hose Car.
Color: Dark Maroon.**

**1915 Webb Chemical and Hose Car for
Oakland Fire Department.**

1915-1920 Seagrave Combination Pumper and Hose Cart. Six cylinder water-cooled engine, developing 110 hp. Pump capacity of 900 GPM. Built for City of El Monte, California. Color: Light red with gold trim.

1915 Peter Pirsch Motorized Pumper and Hose Car.

1912 American LaFrance Underwriter Fire Patrol Wagon. Four cylinders, 77 hp. These were used as salvage wagons and were used with ladders and fire extinguishers. Color: Dark maroon, gold striping.

1912-1914 Seagrave 6 cylinder Combination Pumper and Hose Car. Ladders stowed overhead. Color: White, gold trim.

1912-1914 Seagrave combination Pump and Hose Wagon. Six cylinder, 110 hp. Color: Dark maroon.

1912 American LaFrance Chemical Car. Four cylinder, chain drive, 75 hp. Used by the City of San Francisco. Color: Dark maroon.

1912 American LaFrance Chemical Car with hose reel. This 4 cylinder, 75 hp machine was the first piece of motorized equipment purchased by the City of San Francisco. Color: Dark maroon.

1912-1914 Seagrave Combination Pumper and Hose Car, with overhead ladders. Four cylinder, 77 hp, with pump capacity of 600 GPM. Built for City of San Diego. Color: Dark Maroon.

Seagrave Combination Pumper and Hose Car with added chemical tank. Ladders stowed overhead are 20' extension and 12' with folding hooks. Four cylinder 77 hp engine and a pump capacity of 300 GPM. Color: Light red.

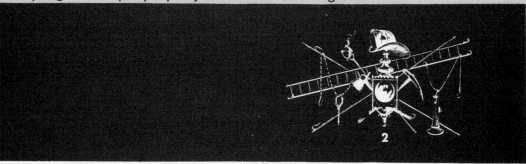

2

30

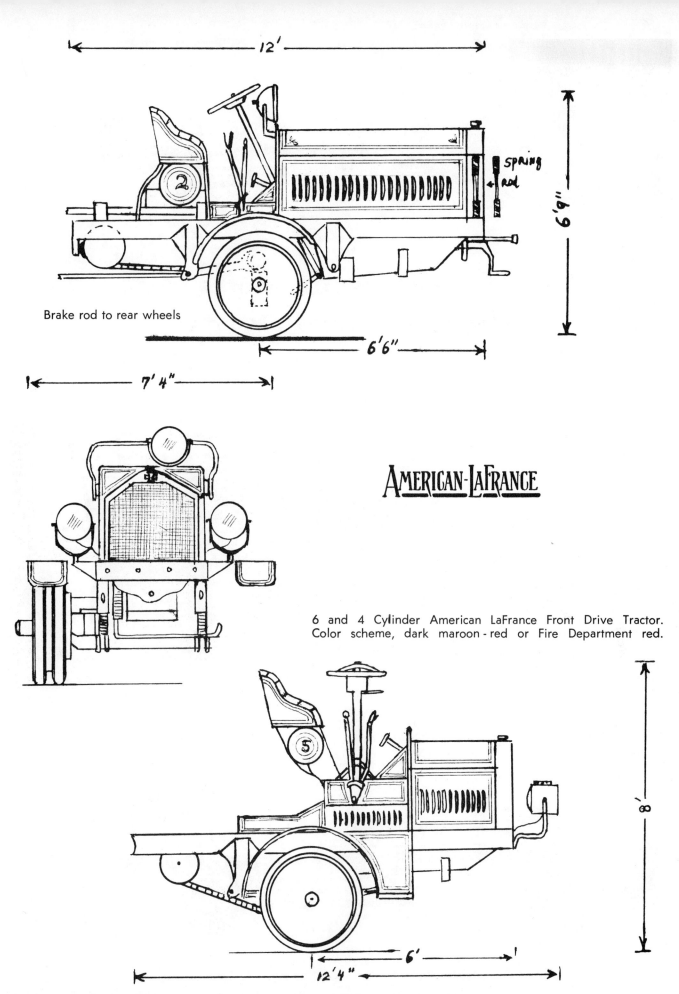

12'

6'9"

spring rod

②

Brake rod to rear wheels

6'6"

7'4"

American-LaFrance

6 and 4 Cylinder American LaFrance Front Drive Tractor.
Color scheme, dark maroon - red or Fire Department red.

⑤

8'

6'

12'4"

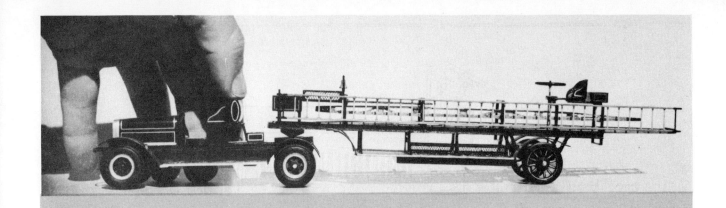

DETAILED SCALE MODELS
MADE BY AUTHOR DaCOSTA

Tractor drawn hook and ladder 1914 and 1925

**Pumper and
hose car model**

1917 American LaFrance Battery Hose Wagon

33

American LaFrance Combination Chemical Engine and Hose Car.

1914-1919 Left, Seagrave Chemical-Hose-Battery Wagon with Gorter type turret nozzle. Right, Seagrave 8 Hose-Pumper. Both from Engine Co. 15, Los
Angeles Fire Department. Color: Dark maroon.

1915-1920 Seagrave 4 cylinder, 77 hp Chemical and Hose Combination. 36x5 solid tires on front, 36x4 dual solids on rear. Color Light red, gold trim.

1919 Seagrave Hose Wagon with Chemical Hose Reel, with ladders stowed overhead. Six cylinder engine, 116 hp, with 950 gallon pumping engine. Seagrave Hose Car, six cylinder, 116 hp engine.

American LaFrance Combination Chemical and Hose Car.

THE SEAGRAVE COMPANY
BUILDERS
COLUMBUS OHIO, U.S.A.
NO. 14477

1912-1914 Seagrave Combination Pumper and Hose Car. 900 GPM pump capacity, six cylinder. Color: Maroon

1912-1914 Seagrave six cylinder Model 360, Pumper and Hose Car. City of
Oxnard, California. Color: Dark Maroon.

1912-1914 Seagrave Hose Wagon with Chemical Cylinder.

Ex-horsedrawn city service hook and ladder pulled by a 1914 American
LaFrance Tractor. Some of these units are still in service, with pneumatic tires,
and drawn by 1961-62 Seagrave tractors. This photo was taken in San
Francisco in 1921.

37

1914 Seagrave Combination Pumper and Hose Car. Six cylinder, 110 hp, with
pump capacity of 900 GPM. Color: Dark maroon.

1914 Seagrave 6 cylinder Pumper and Hose Combination. Chain drive, 116
horse power, with centrifugal pump of 900 GPM capacity.

Seagrave 6 cylinder Tractor for Aerial Truck-Hook and Ladder Service Trucks.
Vintage of 1914.

1914-1917 American LaFrance Battery and Hose Car with Gorter type turret nozzles having three outlets on each side. This car carried 20' extension ladder and an assortment of different size nozzles, wrenches, as well as a high pressure wheel. Color: Dark maroon, with red panels.

A 1915-20 Seagrave 6 cylinder, 110 hp Centrifugal Pumper Engine-Hose Car. Tires were solid and wheels tenoned wood spoke.

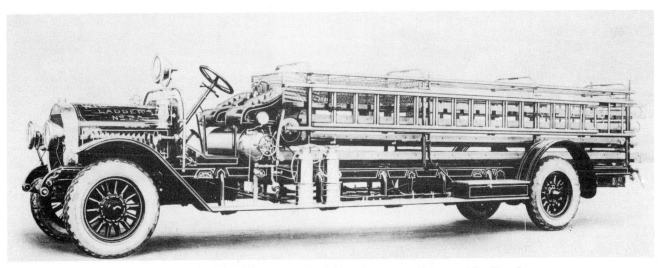

1915-1921 Maxim Motor Co. Model WHL6 City Service Ladder Truck. Color: Dark maroon.

Maxim Model CE4 of 1916 to 1921.

1917 White-Pirsch Chemical and
Hose Car. Built for Pittsburg, Kansas.

American LaFrance Tractor of 1917 vintage.

40

1918 Maxim with rear mounted booster hose reel and water tank (60 gallon) under driver's seat. Color: Dark maroon.

1919 Seagrave 6 cylinder, 110 hp chain-drive City Service straight frame Hook and Ladder.

1919-1920 Seagrave Combination Hose and Pumping Engine. Pump capacity 750 GPM. Carries two 10' suction hoses, and 1200 feet of hose. City of San Jose, Calif. Color: Dark Maroon.

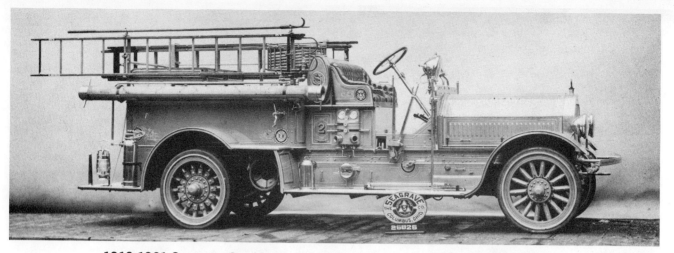

1919-1921 Seagrave Combination Pumper and Hose Car. Six cylinder, 110 hp. Built for the Fire Department of San Leandro, California. Color: Light red, gold trim.

1919-1923 Seagrave straight bed city service Hook and Ladder-Chemical hose reel. Used by city of Pasadena, California and is still in reserve service. Color: Light red, with gold leaf trim.

1920 Peter Pirsch Motorized 500 gallon Triple, with four wheel drive.

1920 Pirsch-Winona Aerial Ladder Truck. Similar in appearance to Seagrave apparatus.

1920 American LaFrance Straight Frame City Service Ladder and Chemical Combination.

1921-1927 Maxim. Models M1, M2, and M3 had 500, 600, and 750 GPM rotary pumps respectively. Engine was 6 cylinder.

Left to right. 1922 White Chemical and Hose Combination. 1919 Seagrave Pumping and Hose Combination. 1914 Seagrave Tractor-drawn City Service hook and ladder Truck.

Maxim models C1, C2, C3-350, 400, 450 GPM rotary pumps, 1922-1927. Four cylinder engines, unit power plant with clutch and transmission, propeller shaft drive, worm gear axles, pneumatic tires and left hand steering. Color: Dark maroon.

1922-1923 American LaFrance Hose Wagon and High Pressure Battery Wagon with Deluge Gun. Four hose couplings on each side.

44

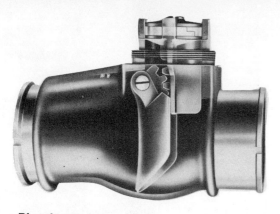 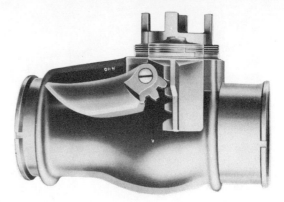

Playpipe on hose closed.   **Maxim Relief Valves, flow type, playpipe on hose line open. (1917-1932)**

1923 American LaFrance Combination Pumper and Hose Car at work in the San Francisco industrial district. In the background, a 1925 American LaFrance. Color: Dark maroon.

1923 Seagrave six cylinder Centrifugal Pumper and Hose Car, with chemical booster and hose reel.

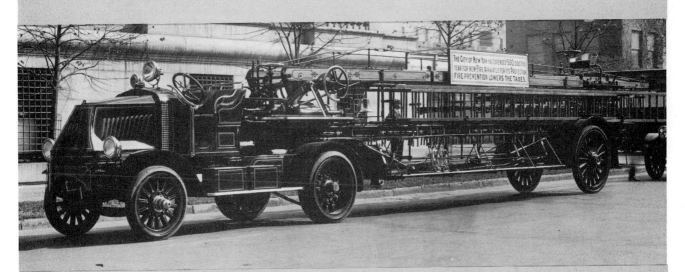

A 1923 vintage Mack AC-6 65 foot Aerial Ladder Truck, Tractor-drawn. Ladder unit is ex-horsedrawn and retains original rear wagon type wheels.

1923-1929 Seagrave 6 cylinder suburban Ladder and Chemical Truck, with double-bank ladder compartments. Ladders carried: 55 foot extension trussed; 35 foot extension trussed; 20 foot wall ladder trussed (2); 12 foot wall trussed, with folding hook; 16 foot wall ladder.

1923-25 Mack AC-6 Aerial Hook and Ladder.

Mack

1924 Ahrens-Fox 750 Gallon Pumper and Hose Car.

A rare shot of 1924-25 Mack Bulldog 75 foot Aerial Ladder Truck as used by the City of New York Fire Department.

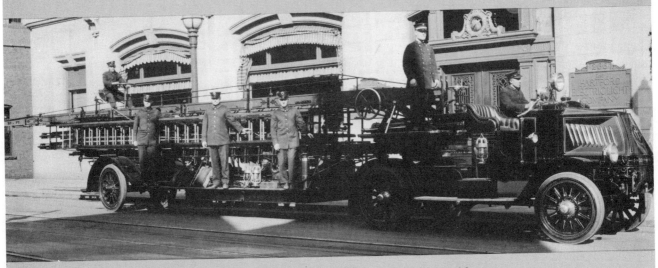

Mack AC-6 Type 4 cylinder Aerial Hook and Ladder.

1924-1925 Seagrave tractor drawn Hook and Ladder. Solid disc wheels, solid tires, and automatic spring hoist aerial mechanism with safety brake for raising and lowering aerial ladder. Six cylinder, 110 hp engine. Color: Light red, gold leaf trim.

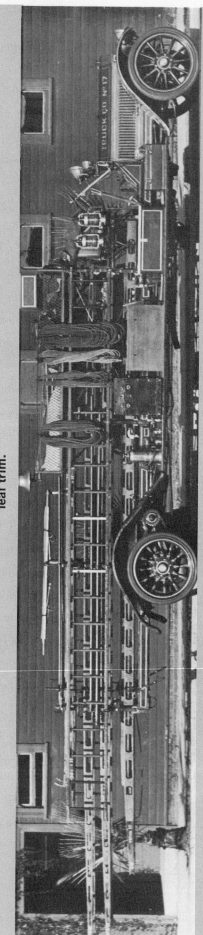

1924-1925 American LaFrance straight frame (no rear steer tiller) City Service Hook and Ladder assigned to Los Angeles Truck Co. #17.

Close-up of 1924-25 Mack Aerial Ladder showing hoist mechanism.

Top view of ladder mechanism of Mack 1924-25 Aerial Hook and Ladder.
Brakes control spring when ladder is raised.

A 1924-25 Mack AC-6 Tractor pulling an American LaFrance
horse-drawn water tower.

1925 Seagrave Tractor-drawn Aerial Hook and Ladder. Trailer was originally horse-drawn with artillery wheels on the rear.

1925 American LaFrance Combination Pumper-Chemical Hose Car. Type 75, 6 cylinder, chain drive.

1925 American LaFrance Type 75 Combination Pumper-Chemical and Hose Car.

1925 American LaFrance Combination Pumper, Chemical and Hose Car. Six cylinders, chain driven. Color: Dark Maroon, Gold trim.

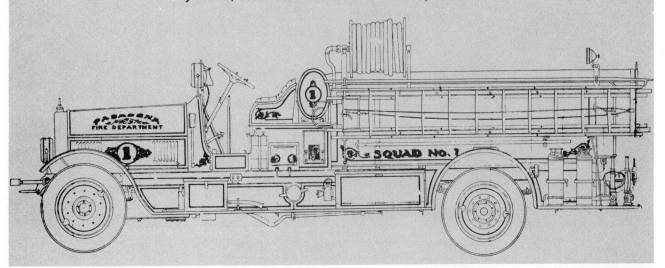

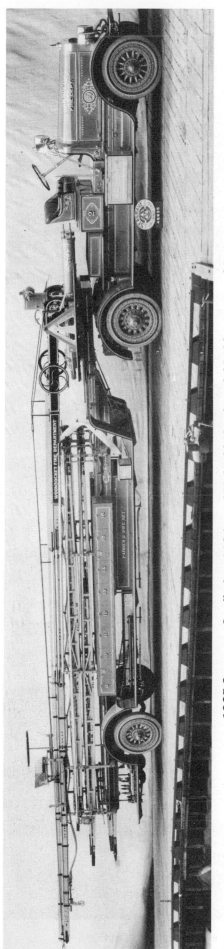

1925 Seagrave 6 cylinder, 110 h.p., 85' double bank aerial ladder tractor drawn truck. Automatic hydraulic hoist aerial mechanism. Note the play pipe nozzle with hose for water tower rise. Color: Light red, gold leaf trim.

1925 American LaFrance Chain Drive Type 75 Pumper-Chemical and Hose Wagon with rotary gear pump of 750 gallon capacity. Six cylinders, 105 hp.

American LaFrance Type 75 Combination Pumping Engine and Hose Car. Built for City of San Francisco in 1925 and retired in 1960.

Detail photo of 5th wheel of tractor and trailer, showing equipment box and tiller signal horn. Note fancy gold leaf trim.

1925 Seagrave Triple Combination Pumper and Hose Car.

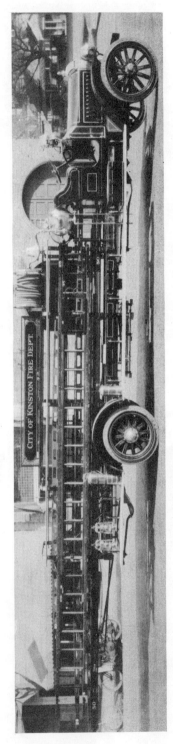

1925 Mack AB Type, 4 wheel City Service Hook and Ladder.
Four cylinders, 60 hp.

1925 1000 GPM Combination Pumper and Hose Car.

Mack AC Type Tractor with an 1898 Hayes Ladder Truck.

58

1925 Mack AC-7 Bulldog Tractor-drawn 75 foot Aerial Truck. Hoist was hand operated.

A 1925 Mack AC-6 Tractor pulling a Seagrave Aerial Trailer. Used by the City of Chicago Fire Department.

A rare photo showing a 1925 Mack AC Tractor pulling an early horse-drawn Hayes Aerial unit.

Mack Bulldog showing front end detail.

American LaFrance Type 75 Combination Pumper-Chemical Hose Car, built in 1925.

1925 American LaFrance Type 75 Triple Combination Pumper-Hose-Chiemcal Wagon.

1925 Mack AC-6. Four cylinder, four wheel tractor for Aerial Truck, City Service, Hook and Ladder and Water Towers.

Detail of 1925 Seagrave 1000 gallon Pumper-Chemical, Hose Combination.
Fireman gets an assist from interested small fry.

A 1925 American LaFrance Type 75 Combination Pumper-Chemical and Hose
Car. Six cylinder, chain-drive, with 105 hp.

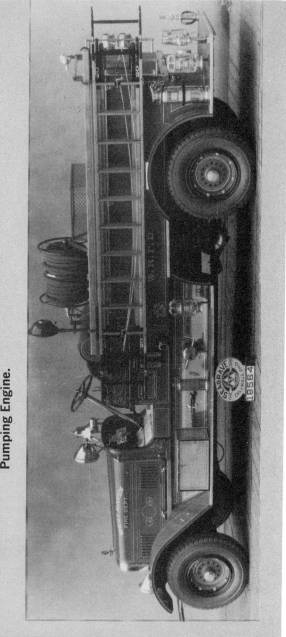

A 1925 Seagrave 6 cylinder Triple Combination Hose, Chemical, and Pumping Engine.

Rear view of a 1925 six cylinder Seagrave Triple Combination Pumper-Hose and Chemical Car.

1925 American LaFrance Type 75 six cylinder chain-drive. Combination Pumper-Chemical and Hose Car.

Left to right. 1925 Stutz City Service Hook and Ladder, straight frame with tiller. 1925 Seagrave Pumper, Chemical and Hose Combination.

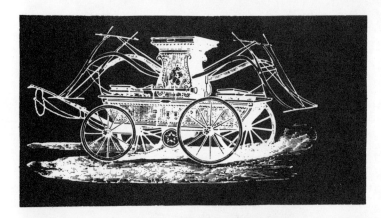

Left to right. American LaFrance 75 Combination Pump-Chemical and Hose Wagon. (1925) Seagrave Triple Combination Pump-Chemical and Hose Wagon. (1925 Seagrave Chemical and Hose Combination. (1919) Los Angeles Fire Department.

1925 Six cylinder 110 hp Tractor Drawn Seagrave 75 foot aerial ladder.

1925-1927 American LaFrance Type 17 aerial 75 foot automatic spring hoist wood ladder truck. Six cylinder, 115 hp. Ladders carried: 16 foot roof ladder; 20 foot; 32 foot; 24 foot; 28 foot; 35 foot extension and 50 foot extension.

Left to Right. 1926 American LaFrance Pumper and Hose Combination. 1926 Stutz Chemical and Hose Combination. 1914 American LaFrance Front-drive Tractor with an 1898 Gorter Water Tower. This unit is still in use by the Los Angeles Fire Department. The tower is raised by water pressure.

1925-1926 American LaFrance Combination Hook and Ladder Truck-Pumper-Hose Combination. Technically known as a Quadruple.

1926 Maxim Double Banked City Service Hook and Ladder No. 1. Watertown, Mass.

Maxim Combination of about 1926 vintage.

1926 Six cylinder Hale 750 GPM Pumper and Hose Car. Note close resemblance to American LaFrance.

1927 Mack Bulldog Pumper-Hose Car. AC Type.

A 1927 Mack Bulldog Pumper and Hose Combination.

AC Type, Mack Bulldog Triple Combination Pumper and Hose Wagon of 1927.

1927 Mack Bulldog. AC type Pumping and Hose Combination built for City of
San Francisco. Color: Maroon

1927-1928 American LaFrance City Service 4 Wheel hook and Ladder. 105 hp,
six cylinder, chain drive. Color: White, with gold leaf trim.

1927-1931 Maxim Pumper and Hose Car.

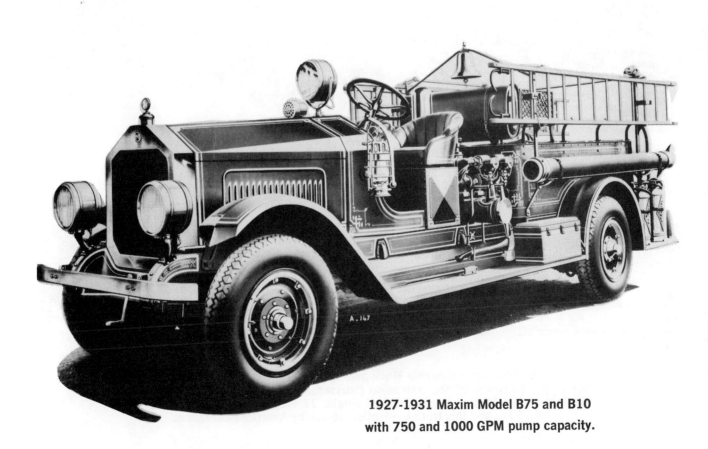

**1927-1931 Maxim Model B75 and B10
with 750 and 1000 GPM pump capacity.**

Semi-cab 1928 Mack AC Type Gorter 30 foot Water Tower of San Francisco Fire Department.

A 1928 American LaFrance City Service Hook and Ladder 4 wheel, with Chemical Tank and Hose Reel.

Two wheel, front-drive Hibernia Hook and Ladder, Type 31. Four cylinders, 75 hp. Ladders carried: 50 foot extension (trussed); 32 foot single; 28 foot single; 24 foot single; 20 foot single; 16 foot single; 12 foot single. Wheelbase is 31 ft., 9 in., and this truck is identical to one by American LaFrance.

Seagrave Squad and Searchlight car.

L-4061

**A 1929 Mack Type 19 Aerial Hook and Ladder with 75 foot hydraulic hoist,
double bank Aerial.**

1932 Seagrave Triple Combination Pumper and Hose Car.

1932 Seagrave, 6 cylinder, 110 hp Combination Pumper and Hose Car with an extra-long suction hose carried forward.

The Seagrave Corporation

COLUMBUS, OHIO

Mack Tractor-drawn City Service Ladder Truck for the City of San Francisco. Tractor is 1935 model, while Ladder Truck is of horse-drawn era.

A detailed view of rear trailer of San Francisco Hook and Ladder, pulled by 1932 Mack Model 19.

1930-33 Mack Type 90 Rescue Squad Wagon rebuilt from pumper a few years back. Now retired from service. San Francisco, Calif.

SECTION

III

100 YEARS OF AMERICA'S
FIRE FIGHTING
APPARATUS

1935-36 Seagrave Quad Ladder-Pumper-Chemical-Hose Combination.

1937 Mack Pumper. Note windscreen for men on rear platform.

1938-39 Ahrens-Fox City Service Ladder with enclosed ladder compartment.

Ahrens-Fox built for New York World's Fair, now used by City of New York.

Ahrens-Fox 1000 GPM Pumper.

1939 Ahrens-Fox 1000 GPM Pumper and Hose Car.

A 1955 Ward-LaFrance Pumper-Hose Combination with semi-cab.

1939 Ahrens-Fox Pumper and Hose Car.

1948 American LaFrance Canopy Cab Water Tower. This unit was originally a City Service Ladder and Water Tower Combination. It was changed over to a straight Water Tower in 1949.

1959-60 Mack Canopy Cab Pumper-Hose Triple Combination.

1960 Mack Canopy Cab Pumper and Hose with Booster Reel.

1960-63 Mack-Magirus 100 foot Aerial, showing detail of hoist mechanism.

1960-63 Mack-Magirus Aerial 100 foot Cab over Engine.

**1960-63 Seagrave 100 foot metal alloy Aerial Ladder.
Hoisting mechanism is electric.**

1960-63 Mack-Magirus 100 foot aerial.

1961-62 Seagrave Cab Canopy Pumper-Hose Triple Combination Engine.

1961-63 Mack Triple Combine Pumper.

1961-63 Mack Pumper and Hose Car.

1961-63 Mack Aerial Ladder with automatic ladder control.

White Model 3000 Small Town Aerial and Pumper Combination.

Model 3014 White Tilt-cab Rescue Wagon.

1962-63 Mack Cab-in-Front Triple Combination Pumper-Hose Car with Booster reel.

1962-63 Mack Triple Combination.

1962-63 Mack Triple Combination.

Mack

1963 Mack semi-cab Centrifugal Pumper-Hose Truck, Triple Combination 500 to 1250 GPM capacity with 300 gallon booster tank.

1963 Mack Pumper and Hose with booster.

1963 Triple Combination Pumper and Hose Wagon.

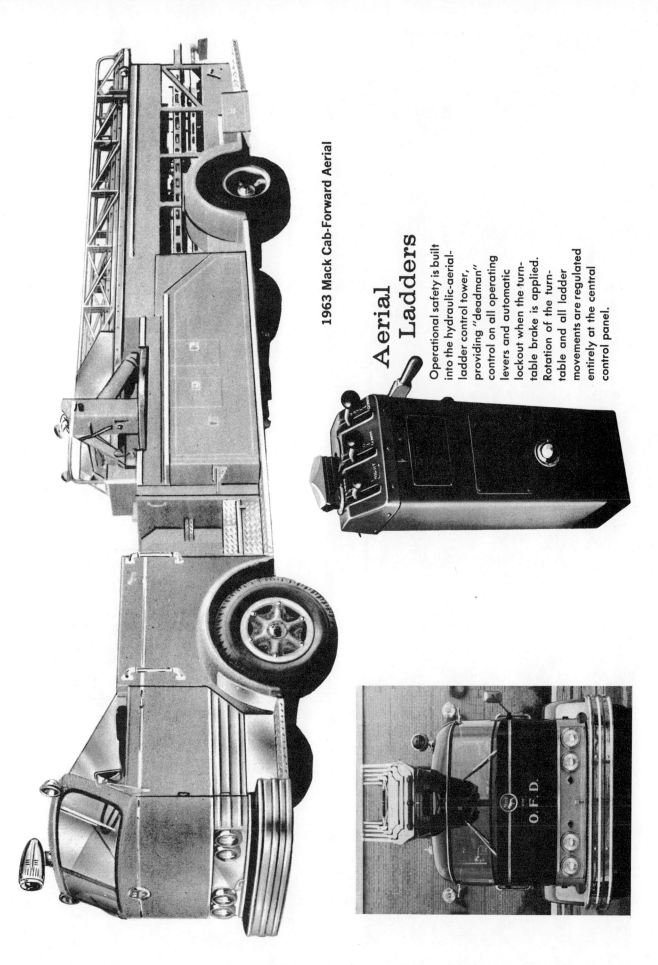

1963 Mack Cab-Forward Aerial

Aerial Ladders

Operational safety is built into the hydraulic-aerial-ladder control tower, providing "deadman" control on all operating levers and automatic lockout when the turntable brake is applied. Rotation of the turntable and all ladder movements are regulated entirely at the central control panel.

Mack Magirus aerial 100 ft. automatic hydraulic — safety alloy steel ladder — rear turntable — nontiller.

Framing of the cab forward design consists of a network of 1-inch square steel tubing which comprises the skeleton for the cab sheeting. This framework and a channel, incorporated as part of the chassis, together with the outer bumper completely encases the driver in a protective shell.

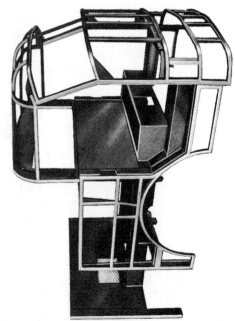

86

Photo of Macks Finest Centrifugal pumps used on their latest equipment.

All the Mack-built features of the famous Thermodyne design are incorporated in this 540 cu. in. overhead-valve and dual ignition engine. These powerplants, so outstanding in the fire-fighting field, develop 204 horsepower at 2800 r.p.m., and have demonstrate stamina and reserve-power

Mack 1963 Triple Combination Pumper-Cab Forward

SECTION

IV

THE bodies used on all but the Hook-and-Ladder and Squad Car types of fire apparatus are constructed of only five sheets of heavy gauge steel plate, ³⁄₁₆ inch thick, electric welded to form the sides and front, and firmly clamped to the side-members of the chassis frame. Another steel plate of the same height extends through the center of the body from front to rear, forming a partition which divides the interior into two equal sections. This affords a more convenient means of stowing the hose and allows two lines to be laid at the same time.

The floor of the body is of hardwood slats laid lengthwise with space between each slat to permit circulation of air throughout the body and thus prevent the wet hose from becoming mildewed. The body has a

Ample Capacity

capacity of 1,000 feet of 2½-inch double-jacketed cotton, rubber-lined hose. Bodies of greater capacity may be had on special order. Vertical rollers are provided at the ends of the body-sides and center partition to assure free movement of the hose when being run out of the body. There are no sharp edges inside the body to damage the hose.

The sides and center partition of the body are reinforced at the top by steel angle irons, and surmounted with horizontal grab-rails of highly-nickeled brass tubing which extend full length of the body, the side rails curving downward at the back and secured to the rear step. A cross rail at the rear of the body is attached to steel uprights at each side and braced at the center by a vertical tube, which also supports the horizontal railing above the center partition. Atop the two rear stanchions decorative light fixtures aid night service by illuminating the interior of the body.

A low, wide step extends across the rear from wheel to wheel, on the sides of which space is provided for carrying the smaller pieces of hand-equipment, such as nozzles, chemical tanks, etc. Extending the width of the body and mounted on this step is a large box, the side of which forms a hinged cover and in which hand tools, jacks, salvage equipment, etc., may be conveniently carried. The entire step and top of the tool box are covered with heavy rubber safety tread bound at the edges with nickeled sheet brass.

Body Equipment

Front and rear fenders are of pressed-steel and supported on the frame and body by husky forged-iron brackets. Wide running boards between the front and rear fenders are covered with rubber safety treads with nickeled-brass bindings, the same as on the rear step. A steel box of substantial size is mounted on each running board, one designed to carry the storage battery, while the other is for small tools, etc.

Two bucket seats of approved fire department design are furnished, having cushions and backs deeply padded with curled hair and upholstered in genuine leather. The high sides and back give the driver a sense of security when traveling at high speed.

An appropriate, hand-operated fire-siren surmounts the dash within easy reach of the assistant-driver. At the left of the siren is

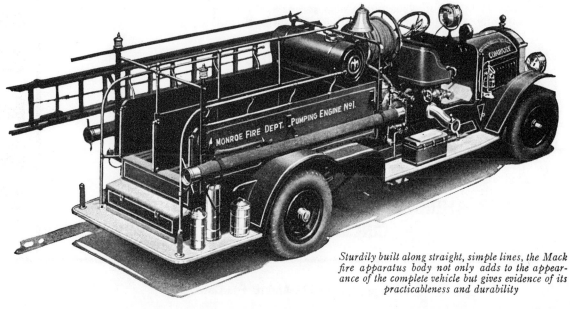

Sturdily built along straight, simple lines, the Mack fire apparatus body not only adds to the appearance of the complete vehicle but gives evidence of its practicableness and durability

SERIES V AND Y PUMPER, HOSE CAR AND BOOSTER APPARATUS

Evidence of the reserve power and extra strength built into Apparatus of the V and Y SERIES is given in the condensed specifications shown below. More complete details will gladly be sent upon request.

ENGINE: The engine furnished with Apparatus of the V and Y Series is essentially a Fire Service unit with adequate power for maximum performance under the most rigorous requirements of Fire Department duty. Vertical "Ell" Head design. Six cylinders 4⅝" bore x 5¼" stroke. Displacement 529.2 cu. in. 131 b.h.p. @ 2300 r.p.m. N.A.C.C. rating 51.3.

FIRE PUMP: Two-stage Centrifugal, or Rotary Pump, optional, with nominal rated capacity of 500 g.p.m. for Model V and 600 g.p.m. for Model Y. Guaranteed to comply with requirements of the National Board of Fire Underwriters and deliver . . .

Model V	Model Y	
500 g.p.m.	600 g.p.m.	at 120 lb. net pump pressure.
250 g.p.m.	300 g.p.m.	at 200 lb. net pump pressure.
167 g.p.m.	200 g.p.m.	at 250 lb. net pump pressure.

CENTRIFUGAL PUMP: Two-stage, with "Double Purpose" combination Primer and Booster Pump auxiliary.

ROTARY PUMP: Self-contained unit with integral geared drive. Pump body of rust resisting alloy and Rotors of solid bronze. Rotors of type which insures non-pulsating discharge. Automatic Relief Valve.

PUMP AUXILIARIES: Two Suction Intakes, with removable strainers and bronze fitted. Two Discharge Gates. Two lengths Suction Hose, 10 foot lengths, 4½" diameter, with plated bronze couplings. One compound gauge and one discharge pressure gauge for main Fire Pump. One discharge pressure gauge for Auxiliary Pump (on centrifugal models).

IGNITION: Two separate systems, one from Magneto and one from Battery. Dual spark plugs.

FRAME: Pressed channel section with tapered ends, of chrome manganese steel. Depth 7", thickness ¼", bottom flange 3" and top flange 2½".

SPRINGS: Semi-elliptic, silico manganese steel. Front 2½" x 40", Rear 3" x 50".

AXLES: Timken Roller Bearings throughout.

BRAKES: Four wheel Hydraulic with Vacuum Booster. Aggregate braking surface 576 square inches.

WHEELS: Steel disc type.

TIRES: Front, single 7.00 x 20; rear, dual 7.00 x 20.

WHEEL BASE: 162".

TREAD: Front 66½"; rear 69".

BOOSTER SYSTEM: Tank of 100 gallons water capacity, with 150 feet of 1" rubber hose. Shut-off nozzle with ¼" and ⅜" tips. On Centrifugal Pump Models a special auxiliary Booster pump is furnished. This pump also serves as Primer for main pump. Booster hose reel conveniently mounted above Hose Body or under Hose Body at rear.

FIRE FIGHTING APPLIANCES

1—24 foot Extension ladder.
1—14 foot Wall and Roof ladder with folding hooks.
1—Pike Pole.
1—Crow Bar.
1—6 lb. Fire Axe.
2—Electric Fire Department Lanterns.
1—2½ gallon Soda and Acid Extinguisher.
1—2½ gallon Foam Extinguisher.
1—2½" Double Female Connection.
1—2½" Double Male Connection.

THE AHRENS-FOX FIRE ENGINE COMPANY
CINCINNATI, OHIO

Page from a 1939 Ahrens-Fox Catalog.

Combination Pumping Engine and Hose Car

Capacity, 1,000 to 1,200 gallons per minute.

SPECIFICATIONS:

Motor:
6-cylinder. Four-cycle. Water-cooled. Cylinders cast separately. Bore, 6¾ inches; stroke, 8 inches. Rated horsepower, 109.3; brake horsepower, 180.

(See detailed specifications of power plant and chassis on pages 20 to 34 inclusive. Complete specifications of this car will be mailed upon request.)

Ignition:
Two independent systems; Bosch high tension magneto and Westinghouse timer-distributor and battery.

Clutch:
Three-plate disc clutch enclosed.

Transmission:
Selective type. Three speeds forward and one reverse. Wide face gears. Positive interlock.

Wheels:
Artillery type wood wheels. Spokes tenoned and grooved.

Tires:
Solid, any standard make.

Self-Starter:
Westinghouse electric.

Pump:
Multiple stage centrifugal, mounted under driver's seat. One suction intake and two discharge gates on each side of car. All discharge gates are controlled by levers on operator's side of car. Pump casing and impellers are made of bronze. (See complete specifications of pump on pages 29 to 32 inclusive.)

Hose Body:
Sides and end of sheet steel substantially braced. Bottom of hardwood strips spaced for ventilation. Capacity of standard body, 1,200 feet regulation fire hose. Larger body will be furnished when required.

Gasoline System:
Copper tank, capacity, 40 gallons. Gravity feed.

Bumper:
Standard Seagrave Spring Bumper.

Principal Dimensions:
Wheel base, 182 inches; tread front, 62 inches; rear, center to center of inside dual tires, 60 inches; center to center of outside dual tires, 71 inches. Length over all, 22 feet 5 inches; width over all, 6 feet 8 inches.

Fire Equipment:
2—10-foot sections of 6-inch hard suction hose with couplings and strainer; 1—10-foot section of soft suction hose with couplings; 1—Pressure gauge; 1—Compound pressure vacuum gauge; 1—20-foot Seagrave trussed extension ladder; 1—12-foot Seagrave trussed roof ladder with folding hooks; 1—Pike pole in regulation holders; 2—Pick head axes in regulation holders; 1—Crowbar in regulation holders; 2—Lanterns in regulation holders; 1—Locomotive bell or 1—Electric horn or hand siren; 2—Nozzle holders; 1—Complete set of tools; 1—Assortment of socket wrenches; 1—Pair tire chains; 1—Heavy auto screw jack; 1—Speedometer; 2—Fire extinguishers.

Chemical Cylinder:
When chemical cylinder is specified the regulation fire equipment will be furnished.

Electric Lights:
1—10-inch revolving searchlight; 2—10-inch rigid headlights; 1—Tail lamp; 1—Trouble lamp with cord.

Tool Box:
One of large capacity in front of rear step.

Painting and Finish:
Painting, decorating and finish will be done to suit purchaser.

THE SEAGRAVE COMPANY, COLUMBUS, OHIO, U.S.A.

Two Wheel Front Drive Aerial Truck

Built in four sizes: 55, 65, 75 and 85 feet.

SPECIFICATIONS:

Hoist:
The aerial ladder has a full automatic spring hoist. It is less complicated, has fewer parts to wear, break or freeze, and fewer gears to strip than any other aerial hoist made.

Motor:
4 or 6-cylinder. Four-cycle. Water-cooled. Cylinders cast separately. Bore, 5¾ inches; stroke, 6½ inches. Rated horsepower, 4 cylinder, 52.8; brake horsepower, 77; rated horsepower, 6-cylinder, 79.3; brake horsepower, 116.

Ignition:—Two independent systems; Bosch high tension magneto and Westinghouse timer-distributor and battery.

Clutch:—Three-plate disc clutch, enclosed.

Transmission:
Selective type. Three speeds forward and one reverse. Wide face gears. Positive interlock.

Wheels:—Artillery type wood wheels. Spokes tenoned and grooved.

Tires:—Solid, any standard make.

Drive:
Drive is by double side chains from jack shaft sprockets to sprockets on wheel driving shaft.

Axles:
The front axle is of forged steel, equipped with roller bearings in the wheels. A ball universal joint in the wheel driving shaft permits the wheels to be steered and driven at the same time. The rear axle is of the automobile pattern, made of drop forged steel and is equipped with roller bearings.

Self-Starter:—Westinghouse electric.

Gasoline System:
Copper tank, capacity, 20 gallons. Gravity feed.

Bumper:—Standard Seagrave Spring Bumper.

Principal Dimensions:
55-foot—Wheel base, 23 feet; length over all, 47 feet; width, 6 feet 10 inches.
65-foot—Wheel base, 25 feet 6 inches; length over all, 49 feet 6 inches; width, 6 feet 10 inches.
75-foot—Wheel base, 28 feet; length over all, 52 feet; width, 6 feet 10 inches.
85-foot—Wheel base, 30 feet 6 inches; length over all, 54 feet 6 inches; width, 6 feet 10 inches.

Ladder Equipment:
55-foot—35-foot extension, 9 x 9-foot extension, 25-foot wall, 18-foot wall, 16-foot wall, 14-foot wall, 12-foot roof, 12-foot roof.
65-foot—40-foot extension, 9 x 9-foot extension, 28-foot wall, 24-foot wall, 18-foot wall, 16-foot wall, 14-foot roof, 12-foot roof.
75-foot—45-foot extension, 9 x 9-foot extension, 30-foot wall, 24-foot wall, 21-foot wall, 16-foot wall, 16-foot roof, 12-foot roof.
85-foot—50-foot extension, 9 x 9-foot extension, 32-foot wall, 28-foot wall, 24-foot wall, 20-foot wall, 16-foot roof, 14-foot roof.
All ladders are Seagrave Patent trussed pattern, made of best well seasoned Douglas Fir. Special ladder equipment will be furnished when desired. All ladders are held in place by suitable ladder locks.

Fire and Truck Equipment:
1—Suitable wire basket for reception of various tools and other appliances is placed underneath frame between running boards; 1—Large tool box is placed on running boards; 4—Lanterns in regulation holders; 4—Rubber buckets or folding pails; 4—Pick head fire axes in regulation holders; 2—Sledge hammers or two wall picks; 2—Steel crowbars in regulation holders; 2—Shovels in regulation holders; 6—Assorted fire hooks in regulation holders; 2—Crotch poles in regulation holders; 2—Four-tine pitch forks; 1—Tin roof cutter; 1—Wire cutter; 2—3-gallon fire department extinguishers with carrying straps, in regulation holders; 1—Door opener in regulation holders; 1—Steel battering ram; 1—Pull down hook, rope and chain; 150 feet of Manila rope with pulley; 1—Locomotive bell, or 1—Electric horn or hand siren; 1—Complete set of tools; 1—Complete assortment of socket wrenches; 1—Heavy auto screw jack.

Electric Lights:—1—10-inch revolving searchlight; 2—10-inch rigid headlights; 1—Tail lamp; 1—Trouble lamp with cord.

Painting and Finish:—Painting, decorating and finish will be done to suit purchaser.

THE SEAGRAVE COMPANY, COLUMBUS, OHIO, U.S.A.

Hose Car

SPECIFICATIONS:

Motor:
4 or 6-cylinder. Four-cycle. Water-cooled. Cylinders cast separately. Bore, $5\frac{3}{4}$ inches; stroke, $6\frac{1}{2}$ inches. Rated horsepower, 4-cylinder, 52.8; brake horsepower, 77; rated horsepower, 6-cylinder, 79.3; brake horsepower, 116.

(See detailed specifications of power plant and chassis on pages 20 to 34 inclusive. Complete specifications of car will be mailed upon request.)

Ignition:
Two independent systems; Bosch high tension magneto and Westinghouse timer-distributor and battery.

Clutch:
Three-plate disc clutch, enclosed.

Transmission:
Selective type. Three speeds forward and one reverse. Wide face gears. Positive interlock.

Wheels:
Artillery type wood wheels. Spokes tenoned and grooved.

Tires:
Solid, any standard make.

Self-Starter:
Westinghouse electric.

Hose Body:
Sides and end of sheet steel substantially braced. Bottom of hardwood strips spaced for ventilation. Capacity, 1,200 feet to 2,000 feet of $2\frac{1}{2}$ or 3-inch fire hose. Special chassis are built to accommodate longer bodies than our standard, when required.

Gasoline System:
Copper tank, capacity, 20 gallons. Gravity feed.

Bumper:
Standard Seagrave Spring Bumper.

Principal Dimensions:
Wheel base, 4-cylinder, 143 inches; 6-cylinder, 158 inches. Tread front, 62 inches; rear, center to center of inside dual tires, 60 inches; center to center of outside dual tires, 71 inches. Length over all, 4-cylinder, 19 feet 1 inch; 6-cylinder, 20 feet 4 inches. Width over all, 4 or 6-cylinder, 6 feet 8 inches.

Fire Equipment:
1—20-foot Seagrave trussed extension ladder; 1—12-foot Seagrave trussed roof ladder with folding hooks; 1—Pike pole in regulation holders; 2—Pick head axes in regulation holders; 1—Crowbar in regulation holders; 2—Lanterns in regulation holders; 1—Locomotive bell, or 1—Electric horn or hand siren; 2—Nozzle holders; 1—Tool kit with complete set of tools; 1—Auto kit containing complete assortment of socket wrenches; 1—Pair tire chains; 1—Heavy screw jack; 1—Speedometer; 2—Fire extinguishers.

Electric Lights:
1—10-inch revolving searchlight; 2—10-inch rigid headlights; 1—Tail lamp; 1—Trouble lamp with cord.

Tool Box:
One of large capacity in front of rear step.

Painting and Finish:
Painting, decorating and finish will be done to suit purchaser.

Combination Pumping Engine and Hose Car

Capacity, 700 to 900 gallons per minute.

SPECIFICATIONS:

Motor:
6-cylinder. Four-cycle. Water-cooled. Cylinders cast separately. Bore, $5\frac{3}{4}$ inches; stroke, $6\frac{1}{2}$ inches. Rated horsepower; 79.3; brake horsepower, 116.

(See detailed specifications of power plant and chassis on pages 20 to 34 inclusive. Complete specifications of car will be mailed upon request.)

Ignition:
Two independent systems; Bosch high tension magneto, and Westinghouse timer-distributor and battery.

Clutch:
Three-plate disc clutch enclosed.

Transmission:
Selective type. Three speeds forward and one reverse. Wide face gears. Positive interlock.

Wheels:
Artillery type wood wheels. Spokes tenoned and grooved.

Tires:
Solid, any standard make.

Self-Starter:
Westinghouse electric.

Pump:
Multiple stage centrifugal, mounted under driver's seat. One suction intake on each side of car. Two discharge gates on the right-hand or operator's side and one on the left-hand side of car. All discharge gates are controlled by levers on operator's side. Pump casing and impellers are made of bronze. (See complete specifications of pump on pages 29 to 32 inclusive.)

Hose Body:
Sides and end of sheet steel substantially braced. Bottom of hardwood strips spaced for ventilation. Capacity of standard body, 1,200 feet regulation fire hose. Larger body will be furnished when required.

Bumper:
Standard Seagrave Spring Bumper.

Principal Dimensions:
Wheel base, 172 inches; tread front, 62 inches rear, center to center of inside dual tires, 60 inches; center to center of outside dual tires, 71 inches. Length over all, 21 feet 8 inches; width over all, 6 feet 8 inches.

Gasoline System:
Copper tank, capacity, 30 gallons. Gravity feed.

Fire Equipment:
2—10-foot sections of 5-inch hard suction hose with couplings and strainer; 1—10-foot length of 4-inch soft suction hose with couplings; 1—Pressure gauge; 1—Compound pressure vacuum gauge; 1—20-foot Seagrave trussed extension ladder; 1—12-foot Seagrave trussed roof ladder with folding hooks; 1—Pike pole in regulation holders; 2—Pick head axes in regulation holders; 1—Crowbar in regulation holders; 2—Lanterns in regulation holders; 1—Locomotive bell, or 1—Electric horn or hand siren; 2—Nozzle holders; 1—Complete set of tools; 1—Complete assortment of socket wrenches; 1—Pair of tire chains; 1—Heavy auto screw jack; 1—Speedometer; 2—Fire extinguishers.

Chemical Cylinder:
When chemical cylinder is specified the regulation equipment will be furnished.

Electric Lights:
1—10-inch revolving searchlight; 2—10-inch rigid headlights; 1—Tail lamp; 1—Trouble lamp with cord.

Tool Box:
One of large capacity in front of rear step.

Painting and Finish:
Painting, decorating and finish will be done to suit purchaser.

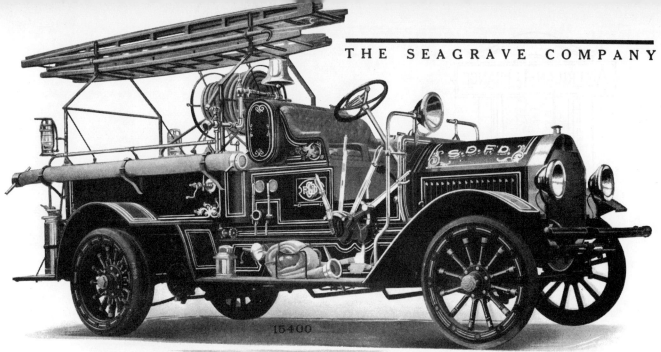

Combination Pumping Engine and Hose Car

Capacity, 500 to 600 gallons per minute.

SPECIFICATIONS:

Motor:

4 or 6-cylinder. Four-cycle. Water-cooled. Cylinders cast separately. Bore, 5¾ inches; stroke, 6½ inches. Rated horsepower, 4-cylinder, 52.8; brake horsepower, 77; rated horsepower, 6-cylinder, 79.3; brake horsepower, 116.

(See detailed specifications of power plant and chassis on pages 20 to 34 inclusive. Complete specifications of car will be mailed upon request.)

Ignition:

Two independent systems; Bosch high tension magneto and Westinghouse timer-distributor and battery.

Clutch:—Three-plate disc clutch, enclosed.

Transmission:

Selective type. Three speeds forward and one reverse. Wide face gears. Positive interlock.

Wheels:

Artillery type wood wheels. Spokes tenoned and grooved.

Tires:—Solid, any standard make.

Self-Starter:—Westinghouse electric.

Pump:

Multiple stage centrifugal, mounted under driver's seat. One suction intake and one discharge gate on each side of car. Both discharge gates are controlled by levers on operator's side. Pump casing and impellers are made of bronze. (See complete specifications for pump on pages 29 to 32 inclusive.)

Hose Body:

Sides and end of sheet steel substantially braced. Bottom of hardwood strips spaced for ventilation. Capacity of standard body, 1,200 feet regulation fire hose. Larger body will be furnished when required.

Gasoline System:

Copper tank, capacity, 20 gallons. Gravity feed.

Bumper:—Standard Seagrave Spring Bumper.

Principal Dimensions:

Wheel base, 4-cylinder, 143 inches; 6-cylinder, 158 inches. Tread front, 62 inches; rear, center to center of inside dual tires, 60 inches; center to center of outside dual tires, 71 inches. Length over all, 4-cylinder, 19 feet 1 inch; 6-cylinder, 20 feet 4 inches. Width over all of 4 or 6-cylinder, 6 feet 8 inches.

Fire Equipment:

2—10-foot lengths of 4-inch rubber suction hose fitted with couplings and strainer; 1—10-foot length of 3-inch cotton rubber lined suction hose of best quality fitted with couplings for hydrant connection; 1—Pressure gauge; 1—Compound pressure vacuum gauge; 1—20-foot Seagrave trussed extension ladder; 1—12-foot Seagrave trussed roof ladder with folding hooks; 1—Pike pole in regulation holders; 2—Pick head axes in regulation holders; 1—Crowbar in regulation holders; 2—Lanterns in regulation holders; 1—Locomotive bell, or 1—Electric horn or hand siren; 2—Nozzle holders; 1—Complete set of tools; 1—Complete assortment of socket wrenches; 1—Pair of tire chains; 1—Heavy auto screw jack; 1—Speedometer; 2—Fire extinguishers.

Chemical Cylinder:

When chemical cylinder is specified the regulation equipment will be furnished.

Electric Lights:—1—10-inch revolving searchlight; 2—10-inch rigid headlights; 1—Tail lamp; 1—Trouble lamp with cord.

Tool Box:

One of large capacity in front of rear step.

Painting and Finish:—Painting, decorating and finish will be done to suit purchaser.

STANDARD TYPE 40

Combination Chemical and Hose Car with Junior Pump

350 Gallons Capacity—Rotary Gear Pump

SPECIFICATIONS

Motor—Four cylinders, 5½-inch bore by 6-inch stroke, 75 Horse Power.

Wheel Base—140½ inches.

Wheels—Artillery Type.

Tires—36 x 4, single front, dual rear. Cup cushion.
Pneumatic, or any special type of tires furnished at additional cost.

Lighting System—
Two 12-inch electric headlights.
One 12-inch electric searchlight.

Gasoline Capacity—30 gallons, gravity feed.

Siren Horn—One, hand-operated.

Locomotive Bell—One.

Tool Box—One.

Equipment Box—One, at rear.

Crowbar—One.

Hose Capacity—1200 feet of 2½-inch hose.

Chemical Tank—One, 40-gallon capacity.

Chemical Hose—200 feet of ¾-inch chemical hose.

Ladders—
One 20-ft. extension ladder.
One 12-ft. roof ladder with folding hooks.

Suction Hose—Two lengths, each 10 ft. 6 in. long.

Pike Pole—One.

Play Pipe Cones—Two.

Axe—One, fire department standard.

Lanterns—Two, Dietz fire department standard.

Extinguishers—Two, 2½-gallon Babcock.

Bumper—Heavy steel with recoil springs.

ALL NECESSARY OPERATING TOOLS

Detailed specifications on request

During the last eight years, New York City has purchased nearly 200 LaFrance pumpers

American-LaFrance

STANDARD TYPE 75

Chemical Car

SPECIFICATIONS

Motor—Six cylinders, 5½-inch bore by 6-inch stroke, 105 Horse Power.

Wheel Base—156½ inches.

Wheels—Artillery Type.

Tires—36 x 4, single front, dual rear. Cup cushion.
Pneumatic, or any special type of tires furnished at additional cost.

Lighting System—
Two 12-inch electric headlights.
One 12-inch electric searchlight.

Gasoline Capacity—15 gallons, gravity feed.

Siren Horn—One, hand-operated.

Locomotive Bell—One.

Equipment Box—One, at rear.

Tool Box—One.

Crowbar—One.

Chemical Tanks—Four, each 60-gallon capacity.

Chemical Hose—400 feet of 1-inch chemical hose.

Ladders—
One 20-ft. extension ladder.
One 12-ft. roof ladder with folding hooks.

Pike Pole—One.

Axe—One, fire department standard.

Lanterns—Two, Dietz fire department standard.

Extinguishers—Two, 2½-gallon Babcock.

Bumper—Heavy steel with recoil springs.

ALL NECESSARY OPERATING TOOLS

This apparatus can be furnished with four-cylinder motor.
Capacity and arrangement of chemical tanks may also be varied.

Detailed specifications on request

Notice how many cities near you are satisfied users of American-LaFrance equipment

STANDARD TYPE 17

Four-Wheel Tractor

SPECIFICATIONS

Motor—Six cylinders, 5½-inch bore by 6-inch stroke, 105 Horse Power.

Wheel Base—156½ inches.

Wheels—Artillery Type.

Tires—36 x 4, single front, dual rear. Cup cushion.
 Any special type of tires furnished at additional cost.

Equipment Basket—One, wire mesh.

Locker—One, under seat.

Lighting System—Two 12-inch electric headlights.

Gasoline Capacity—15 gallons, gravity feed.

Siren Horn—One, hand-operated.

Tool Box—One.

Bumper—Heavy steel with recoil springs.

Fifth wheel and attachment brackets.

ALL NECESSARY OPERATING TOOLS

This tractor is designed so that it can be readily placed under present horse-drawn apparatus.

Tractor can be built with four-cylinder motor.

Detailed specifications on request

American-LaFrance rotary gear pumps have established unusually fine records

STANDARD TYPE 75

Combination Chemical and Hose Car

SPECIFICATIONS

Motor—Six cylinders, 5½-inch bore by 6-inch stroke, 105 Horse Power.

Wheel Base—156½ inches.

Wheels—Artillery Type.

Tires—36 x 4, single front, dual rear. Cup cushion.
Pneumatic, or any special type of tires furnished at additional cost.

Lighting System—
Two 12-inch electric headlights.
One 12-inch electric searchlight.

Gasoline Capacity—30 gallons, gravity feed.

Siren Horn—One, hand-operated.

Locomotive Bell—One.

Tool Box—One.

Equipment Box—One, at rear.

Crowbar—One.

Hose Capacity—1200 feet of 2½-inch hose.

Chemical Tank—One, 40-gallon capacity.

Chemical Hose—200 feet of ¾-inch chemical hose.

Ladders—
One 20-ft. extension ladder.
One 12-ft. roof ladder with folding hooks.

Pike Pole—One.

Play Pipe Cones—Two.

Axe—One, fire department standard.

Lanterns—Two, Dietz fire department standard.

Extinguishers—Two, 2½-gallon Babcock.

Bumper—Heavy steel with recoil springs.

ALL NECESSARY OPERATING TOOLS

This apparatus can be furnished with two chemical tanks; or, for use as a straight hose car, all chemical equipment can be eliminated.

Detailed specifications on request

Cities reorder American-LaFrance fire apparatus when they require additional purchases

Type 38 Motor—Inlet Side

Type 38 Motor—Exhaust Side

· AMERICAN-LAFRANCE ·

Type 38 Motor

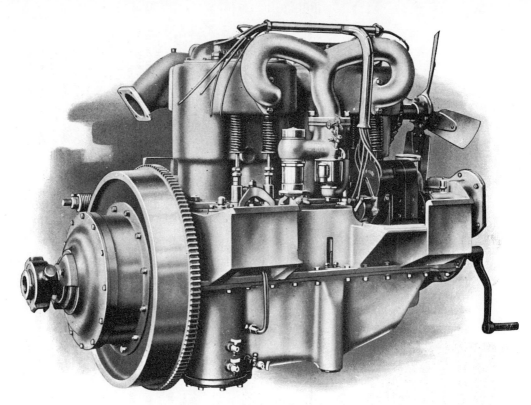

Type 10 Motor—Inlet Side

Type 10 Motor—Exhaust Side

· AMERICAN-LA FRANCE ·

Type 10 Motor

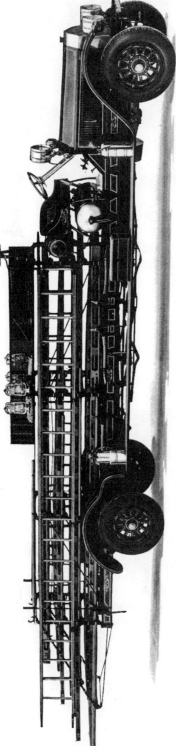

AMERICAN-LaFRANCE

Combination City Service Hook and Ladder Truck

SPECIFICATIONS

Motor—Six cylinders, 5½-inch bore by 6-inch stroke, 105 Horse Power.

Wheel Base—246½ inches.

Wheels—Artillery Type.

Tires—Single front, dual rear. Cup cushion.

Pneumatic, or any special type of tires furnished at additional cost.

Lighting System—
Two 12-inch electric headlights.
One 12-inch electric searchlight.

Gasoline Capacity—20 gallons, gravity feed.

Siren Horn—One, hand-operated.

Locomotive Bell—One, 12-inch.

Chemical Tank—One, 40-gallon capacity.

Chemical Hose—200 feet of ¾-inch chemical hose.

Extinguishers—Two, 2½-gallon Babcock.

Lanterns—Four, Dietz fire department standard.

Axes—Four, fire department standard.

Wall Picks—Two.

Crowbars—Two.

Shovels—Two.

Wire Cutter—One, Boston.

Door Opener—One, Detroit.

Tin Roof Cutter—One, La France.

Pitchforks—Two.

Rubber Buckets—Four.

Pike Poles—Six, assorted lengths.

Crotch Poles—Two.

Wire Basket—One.

Tool Box—One.

Ladder Lock—One.

Bumper—One.

ALL NECESSARY OPERATING TOOLS

This apparatus is built without chemical equipment if desired, and can be furnished with four-cylinder motor.

LADDER EQUIPMENT

One 50-ft. rapid-hoist rope and pulley extension ladder to extend fifty feet, with supporting poles.

One 35-ft. rapid-hoist rope and pulley extension to extend thirty-five feet.

One 28-ft. single ladder.

Two 25-ft. single ladders.

One 24-ft. single ladder.

One 20-ft. single ladder.

One 16-ft. roof ladder.

One 12-ft. roof ladder.

Total ladder equipment, 235 feet.

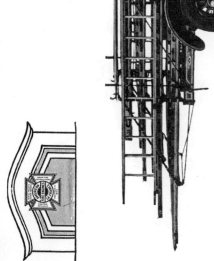

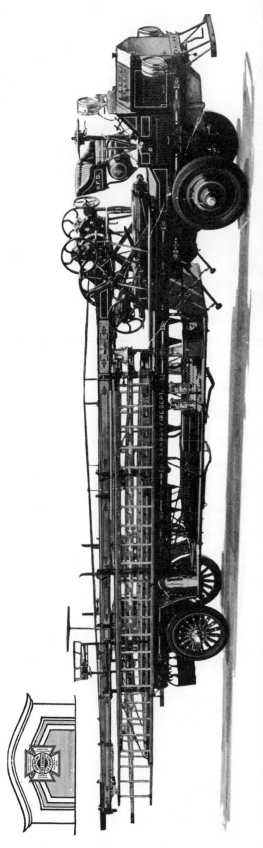

STANDARD TYPE 31

Front Drive Aërial Truck

SPECIFICATIONS

Motor—Six cylinders, 5½-inch bore by 6-inch stroke, 105 Horse Power.

Wheel Base—
55-ft. Aërial truck—19 ft. 9 in.
65-ft. Aërial truck—23 ft. 9 in.
75-ft. Aërial truck—27 ft. 9 in.
85-ft. Aërial truck—31 ft. 9 in.

Wheels—Cast steel disc front, artillery type rear.

Tires—Single Giant front, single rear. Special types of tires furnished at additional cost.

Lighting System—Two 12-inch electric headlights.

Gasoline Capacity—20 gallons, gravity feed.

Extinguishers—Two, 2½-gallon Babcock.

Siren Horn—One, hand-operated.

Locomotive Bell—One, 12-inch.

Lanterns—Four, fire department standard.

Axes—Four, fire department standard.

Wall Picks—Two.

Crowbars—Two.

Shovels—Two.

Wire Cutter—One, Boston.

Door Opener—One, Detroit.

Tin Roof Cutter—One, La France.

Pitchforks—Two.

Battering Ram—One, La France.

Rubber Buckets—Four.

Pike Poles—Six, assorted lengths.

Crotch Poles—Two.

Wire Basket—One, under frame.

Tool Platform—One, under frame.

Tool Box—One.

Charge Box—Two.

Manila rope, tackle, and snatch block.

Ladder Lock—One.

Bumper—One.

ALL NECESSARY OPERATING TOOLS

This truck can also be furnished with a four-cylinder motor.

Detailed specifications on request

LADDER EQUIPMENT

85-FT. TRUCK
50-ft. extension ladder
32-ft. single ladder
28-ft. single ladder
24-ft. single ladder
20-ft. single ladder
16-ft. single ladder
12-ft. roof ladder
Total ground ladder equipment, 182 feet.

75-FT. TRUCK
45-ft. extension ladder
32-ft. single ladder
28-ft. single ladder
24-ft. single ladder
20-ft. single ladder
16-ft. single ladder
12-ft. roof ladder
Total ground ladder equipment, 177 feet.

65-FT. TRUCK
40-ft. extension ladder
28-ft. single ladder
24-ft. single ladder
20-ft. single ladder
16-ft. single ladder
12-ft. roof ladder
Total ground ladder equipment, 140 feet.

55-FT. TRUCK
35-ft. extension ladder
24-ft. single ladder
20-ft. single ladder
16-ft. single ladder
12-ft. roof ladder
Total ground ladder equipment, 107 feet.

AMERICAN-LaFrance

More than 50 cities have American-LaFrance fleets of ten or more pieces

STANDARD TYPE 39

Triple Combination Pumping, Chemical and Hose Car

600 Gallons Capacity—Rotary Gear Pump

SPECIFICATIONS

Motor—Four cylinders, 5½-inch bore by 6-inch stroke, 75 Horse Power.

Wheel Base—140½ inches.

Wheels—Artillery Type.

Tires—36 x 4, single front, dual rear. Cup cushion.
Pneumatic, or any special type of tires furnished at additional cost.

Lighting System—
Two 12-inch electric headlights.
One 12-inch electric searchlight.

Gasoline Capacity—30 gallons, gravity feed.

Siren Horn—One, hand-operated.

Locomotive Bell—One.

Tool Box—One.

Equipment Box—One, at rear.

Crowbar—One.

Hose Capacity—1100 feet of 2½-inch hose.

Chemical Tank—One, 40-gallon capacity.

Chemical Hose—200 feet of ¾-inch chemical hose.

Ladders—
One 20-ft. extension ladder.
One 12-ft. roof ladder with folding hooks.

Suction Hose—Two lengths, each 10 ft. 6 in. long.

Pike Pole—One.

Play Pipe Cones—Two.

Axe—One, fire department standard.

Lanterns—Two, Dietz fire department standard.

Extinguishers—Two, 2½-gallon Babcock.

Bumper—Heavy steel with recoil springs.

ALL NECESSARY OPERATING TOOLS

This apparatus can be furnished without chemical equipment if desired.

Detailed specifications on request

New York City has over two hundred and fifty pieces of LaFrance motor apparatus

STANDARD TYPE 38

Triple Combination Pumping, Chemical and Hose Car

with Type 39 Pump

600 Gallons Capacity—Rotary Gear Pump

SPECIFICATIONS

Motor—Six cylinders, 4½-inch bore by 6-inch stroke, 75 Horse Power.

Wheel Base—156½ inches.

Wheels—Artillery Type.

Tires—36 x 4, single front, dual rear. Cup cushion.
Pneumatic, or any special type of tires furnished at additional cost.

Lighting System—
Two 12-inch electric headlights.
One 12-inch electric searchlight.

Gasoline Capacity—30 gallons, gravity feed.

Siren Horn—One, hand-operated.

Locomotive Bell—One.

Tool Box—One.

Equipment Box—One, at rear.

Crowbar—One.

Hose Capacity—1200 feet of 2½-inch hose.

Chemical Tank—One, 40-gallon capacity.

Chemical Hose—200 feet of ¾-inch chemical hose.

Ladders—
One 20-ft. extension ladder.
One 12-ft. roof ladder with folding hooks.

Suction Hose—Two lengths, each 10 ft. 6 in. long.

Pike Pole—One.

Play Pipe Cones—Two.

Axe—One, fire department standard.

Lanterns—Two, Dietz fire department standard.

Extinguishers—Two, 2½-gallon Babcock.

Bumper—Heavy steel with recoil springs.

ALL NECESSARY OPERATING TOOLS

This apparatus can be furnished without chemical equipment if desired.

Detailed specifications on request

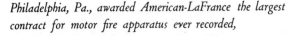

Philadelphia, Pa., awarded American-LaFrance the largest contract for motor fire apparatus ever recorded,

STANDARD TYPE 31

Front-Drive Tractor for Aërial Truck

SPECIFICATIONS

Motor—Four cylinders, 5½-inch bore by 6-inch stroke, 75 Horse Power.

Wheels—Cast steel, solid disc type.

Tires—Single Giant.
  Special types of tires furnished at additional cost.

Lighting System—Two 12-inch electric headlights.

Siren Horn—One, hand-operated.

Tool Box—One.

Gasoline Capacity—20 gallons, gravity feed.

Bumper—One.

ALL NECESSARY OPERATING TOOLS

This tractor can be furnished with six-cylinder motor.

Detailed specifications on request

STANDARD TYPE 31

Front-Drive Tractor for Steamer

SPECIFICATIONS

Motor—Four cylinders, 5½-inch bore by 6-inch stroke, 75 Horse Power.

Wheels—Cast steel, solid disc type.

Tires—Single Giant.
Special types of tires furnished at additional cost.

Lighting System—
Two 12-inch electric headlights.

Siren Horn—One, hand-operated.

Tool Box—One.

Gasoline Capacity—20 gallons, gravity feed.

Bumper—One.

ALL NECESSARY OPERATING TOOLS

This tractor can be furnished with six-cylinder motor if desired.

Detailed specifications on request

Our steamer tractors are provided with oscillating trunnion to provide for sway and strain.

VALVES are located side-by-side on the right of the engine, actuated by roller-type lifters and tubular push rods. Tappets, springs and valve stems are housed in two chambers and are accessible by the removal of cover plates that seal the chambers, each held in place by two large wheel-nuts. Exhaust valves are of chrome-silicon steel and intake of chrome-nickel steel. Fuel is fed by gravity from a 25-gallon tank on hose wagons and ladder trucks, and from a 40-gallon tank on apparatus equipped with fire pumps.

Efficient cooling results from the use of a continuous-finned radiator core and hand-adjustable steel radiator shutters. The staunch brass upper tank and the aluminum lower tank and side-plates combined with a shock-insulating rubber block support assure freedom from derangements

Timing drive is accomplished with but three gears, namely, the crankshaft, camshaft and auxiliary cross-shaft gears.

Three-Gear Timing Drive

The first two are of case-hardened steel, while the third is of bronze, set perpendicular to the other two and driven from the camshaft gear. All three have helical teeth, and to secure silent operation and long life, the steel gears are ground to perfect form and surface.

The cross-shaft gear, with its two Timken bearings, is carried in a separate housing bolted to the timing gear extension of the crankcase. The shaft to which the gear is secured extends

Both the water pump and the magneto are located high, dry and accessible at the front of the engine, each driven independently by the cross-shaft and with short and direct connections

across the front of the engine, driving the water pump at the right, magneto at the left and distributor at the center. Thus located, the accessibility of these units is greatly increased.

Water connections are uncommonly direct. The water pump, located at the front of the engine, draws its supply by a short, straight hose connection from the lower radiator tank and discharges it by a similarly short elbow into the front of the cylinder block. Here, instead of flowing into the jackets directly, it is conducted through a brass header, cast in the cylinder block, from where it issues through four holes directly under the exhaust valve seats.

The introduction of the coolest water into the hottest part of the cylinder means cooler valves, with less warpage and pitting and more uniform distribution of heat throughout the cylinders. Water jackets are of unusual size, particularly about the valve seats, and of more than usual depth.

The radiator is of the continuous-fin tubular type, comprising a separate upper tank of heavy nickel-plated brass, a lower tank and

A single stuffing box. packed with greaseless, ready-cut packing; a balanced bronze rotor; a stainless steel shaft and a thrustless splined drive are a few of the unusual features of the water pump

side plates of cast aluminum, all bolted together and supporting the core. It is mounted on large rubber blocks so that it cannot be strained by frame weaving. Water temperature is controlled by shutters across the front of the radiator operated manually by a knob placed on the dash convenient to the driver. Their intelligent manipulation is assisted by a Motometer surmounting the radiator cap. A 22-inch, pressed steel fan of four blades is driven by a wide, flat belt from a pulley attached to the camshaft gear.

The pump is of the balanced-rotor type and has but one stuffing box, packed with self-lubricating metallic packing. The rotor is of navy bronze, non-corroding and is balanced. Water is taken in on both sides simultaneously, thus excluding all side thrust. The pump shaft is of stainless steel, also non-corroding, and is driven by a splined fitting on the engine cross-shaft coupling. Unusual accessibility is gained by this mounting.

Effective Lubrication
No grease cups are used on the pump, thus eliminating the possibility of grease entering and clogging the radiator or cylinder jackets, another instance of designing for dependability.

Force feed and splash lubrication are combined in a unique manner. Circulation of the oil is produced by a gear pump located at the bottom of the crankcase oil sump, and driven, as already mentioned, from the camshaft. This pump raises the oil in abundant quantity and under moderate pressure from the crankcase sump to an auxiliary reservoir at the upper left front of the cylinder block and cast integrally with it. With only a thin wall separating the reservoir from the water jackets, the oil is quickly warmed on starting the engine, and is maintained under all operating conditions at a practically constant temperature by the cooling water in the cylinder jackets. This eliminates the dangers of sluggish circulation of chilled oil as well as the disastrous effects arising from overheated oil that has lost its lubricating value.

Here is shown the rear support beam in place, the fly-wheel and its bell-housing

From the auxiliary reservoir oil is fed to all three main bearings and to the four splash troughs beneath the connecting rods. Scoops on the ends of the rods, dipping into the oil at each revolution, convey an ample amount to the crankpins and throw the balance in the form of a spray over the valve-lifters, wristpins and cylinder walls. Oil in the splash troughs is kept at a constant level by continuous overflow, the amount of oil fed being always in excess of actual requirements. Surplus oil in the reservoir is conducted through a large tube to the timing gears, bathing them in a constant cataract of oil.

Oil Twice Screened

The oil is twice screened each time it circulates; first, as it is sucked into the pump, and then again as it enters the upper reservoir. Both screens are readily removable for cleaning, the pump screen through a trap at the bottom of the crankcase, while the other is lifted out by unbolting the reservoir cover-plate. With the exception of the short oil pipe leading from the reservoir to the timing gears and the oil gage lead, all oil piping is cast in the crankcase and cylinder block which insures rigidity and freedom from breakage.

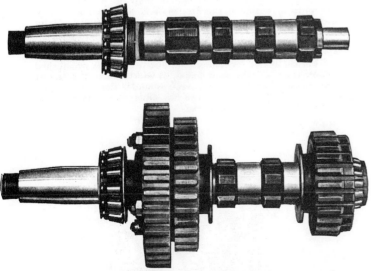

The Mack interrupted spline shaft provides a snug and positive drive for the gears while retaining a firm seating on ground surfaces to keep them in line

1910 Seagrave Side Saddle electric driven Aerial Ladder Truck.

San Francisco's UP-TO-THE-MINUTE FIRE PROTECTION-1921-1922 — Taken for San Francisco Fire Dept. Report.

Short Descriptive History of the Fire Department of the Convention City — It's Splendid Record of Service — Added Efficiency Result of Earthquake Fire — High Pressure System.

By Chief Thomas R. Murphy, Fire Department, San Francisco, year 1922.

The following brief article by Chief Murphy gives a condensed history of the fire department of San Francisco. Much of the success of the Jubilee convention will be due to the efforts of Chief Murphy and his associates, who not only have spared no efforts to insure the comfort of the visiting chiefs but also have thrown themselves into the breach in the endeavor to insure the attendance of as many chiefs as possible. Chief Murphy was born in San Francisco in 1870. He entered the San Francisco fire department as driver of Truck Co. 2 and served consecutively as captain of Chemical Co. No. 6, Chemical Co. No. 3, Engine Co. No. 1 and as battalion chief and second assistant chief. Following closely upon his installation as chief in 1910, came the adoption of motor apparatus, which he pushed so vigorously in the face of many obstacles, that now the department is completely motorized. San Francisco's efficient high pressure system was completed during his early incumbency, and under his guidance the department has achieved and maintained a high standard of efficiency.

The San Francisco fire department was organized in the year 1849, following upon the heels of a disastrous fire, which wiped out the business section of the then struggling community of adventurers and gold seekers. The first hand operated equipment was brought around Cape Horn and Frederick D. Kohler was appointed the first chief engineer. Other chiefs of that period were: Frank E. R. Whitney, George Hossefros, Chas. P. Duane, Jas. E. Nutman and David Scannell.

In 1866 the old volunteer department was superseded by the paid (or call) department. During this, the second period of its existence, horse drawn steam fire engines and ladder trucks were introduced, and all officers and members exception the extra or call men were required to devote their entire time to the service in the department. Chief Scannell was again appointed chief in 1871, and remained at the head of the department until his death in 1893. He was succeeded by Dennis T. Sullivan, a fireman of the highest ability and untiring devotion to duty. In the year 1900 the department again was reorganized upon a fully paid basis, civil service was introduced, and a retirement system which still is in force was installed. Chief Sullivan died in 1906, from injuries received during the earthquate which visited the city on April 18th, of that year, and was succeeded temporarily by Chief John Dougherty, who retired the same year. Chief Patrick H. Shaughnessy was appointed chief on July 15th, 1906, and remained at the head of the department until March 16th, 1910, when he was succeeded by the writer.

Profiting by the lesson of the fire of 1906, a high pressure fire system was installed, which was designed by the foremost engineering authorities with a view to preventing the recurrence of a similar catastrophe, and the same is now in successful operation and has fulfilled every expectation. Motor apparatus began replacing the horse-drawn equipment in 1912 and before the close of 1921 the department was fully motorized.

A bureau of Fire Prevention and Public Safety is established in connection with the department, of which the chief engineer is ex-officio chairman. This bureau is under the direct supervision of a battalion chief, who has under him a force of inspectors from the uniform rank.

THE EQUIPMENT OF SAN FRANCISCO'S WORLD FAMOUS FIRE DEPARTMENT

The equipment in service at the close of 1921 and 1922 consisted of the following pieces for the San Francisco Fire Dept.

A — Two 1905-15 American LaFrance tractorized front drive 6 cylinder Steamers.

B — Two 1905-15 Christie front drive tractorized steamers.

C — Thirty five gasoline propelled pumping engines consisting of the following types. 1912-1917 American LaFrance, 1913-1919 Seagrave pumpers and hose cars, 1915 Ahren & Fox (front pump) car, 1919 Ahren and Fox front pump and hose car.

D — Twelve motor propelled city service hook and ladder trucks drawn by tractors of types consisting of 1914 American LaFrance, 1914-16 Seagrave, 1914-1915 Schnerr, 1913-1915 Knox-Martin three wheel tractor and 1913-1914 White Motor Co. Tractor.

E — One 1914-17 American La France tractor drawn 85 ft. aerial ladder truck.

F — Four straight hose wagons, 1912-1917 American LaFrance which were later changed over to high pressure battery wagons with Gorter type turret nozzles. Also were Webb 1915 seat over engine fire boat tender with Gorter turrets on them and a White (Duck Wagon) fire boat tender with Gorter turret nozzles.

G — Ten motor propelled combination chemical and hose wagons of 1912-1917 vintage consisting of American LaFrance and 1915 Schnerrs.

H — Twelve motor propelled straight chemical cars of 1912-1917 vintage, American La France types. Some were 6 cylinders and 4 cylinder types.

I — Two water towers (Gorter types) One which consisted of 1898 type, 65 ft. height after being raised for fighting fires on five stories
One which consisted of 1902 type, 75 ft. height after being raised for fighting fire on eight stories.

Both were driven by tractorized gasoline propelled Kleiber motor tractors of 1920-1922 vintage. The 1898 water towers was last to be motorized. Both retained the Hartford type wagon wheel with hard solid tires until the year 1945, then changed over to pneumatics. The tractors retained the solid tires with exception of one which pulled large tower. That one was one which pulled large tower. That one was changed to pneumatics. (now gone due to accident)

J — Two steam fire boats one — Dennis T. Sullivan
one — David Scannell

K — Ten chiefs cars 1921 Buicks

L — There were a number of additional pieces for relief purposes. The 1898 water tower was converted from horse to motor after the large tower was motorized. The dept. retained a few large pieces of horse drawn rigs such as the Gorter two wheel battery cart which resembled an artillery piece.

Most all the apparatus mentioned in the 1921 SFFD roster report are illustrated throughout the book although some minor changes have been made such as change over to pneumatics from solid tires.

The motor propelled hook and ladders are still in use today drawn by 1960 and 1961 tractors.

Water tower number one is now drawn by a 1938 Ahrens-Fox tractor since the Kleiber was demolished in street accident. Only two Kleibers exist today. One, a 1926 search light wagon and the 1921 tractor for 65 foot water tower of 1898 vintage. Photos shown in this book of water towers are drawn by Kleibers. Note the one with pneumatics and the other with solid tires. It would be interesting to note that the early 1912-1920 pumpers and hose wagons which the hoses were carried in were wood paneled with fancy scalloped designs and were trimmed up in gold leaf with dark maroon red paint job. The dark maroon red is still used today on all of the San Francisco apparatus but it is rumored that a change to light red is being considered.

SCHEMATIC DRAWING SHOWING GRAPHICALLY WHAT THE CAPABILITIES OF A WATER TOWER ARE

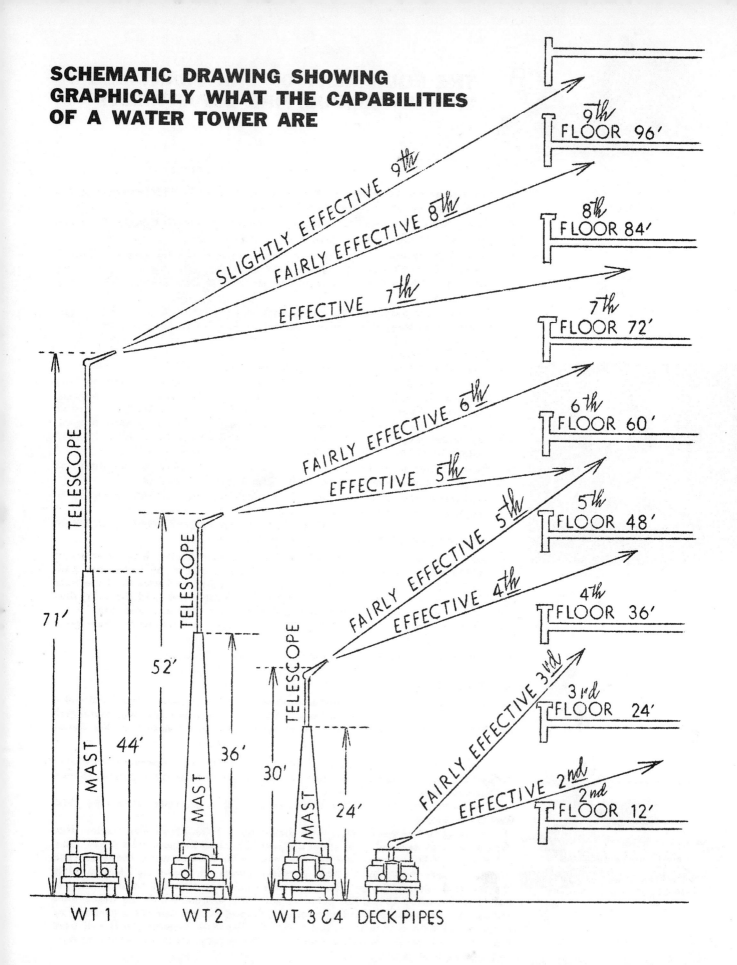